CHRISTIANITY AND SCIENCE

By *JEAN ABELÉ, S.J.*

Translated from the French by R. F. TREVETT

HAWTHORN BOOKS · PUBLISHERS · *New York*

Edited by HENRI DANIEL-ROPS of the Académie Française

CHRISTIANITY AND SCIENCE

IS VOLUME

14

OF THE

Twentieth Century Encyclopedia of Catholicism

UNDER SECTION

I

KNOWLEDGE AND FAITH

IT IS ALSO THE

76TH

VOLUME IN ORDER OF PUBLICATION

First Edition, October, 1961

NIHIL OBSTAT

Joannes M. T. Barton, S.T.D., L.S.S.

> *Censor Deputatus*

IMPRIMATUR

E. Morrogh Bernard

> *Vicarius Generalis*

Westmonasterii, die VIII SEPTEMBRIS, MCMLXI.

CONTENTS

INTRODUCTION

As things are today, it seems that the time has gone when the existence of a so-called hostility between Christianity and science calls for discussion. We no longer live at the period when the heirs of a dictatorship long exercised by the triumvirate Berthelot, Renan and Taine closed the gates of the Sorbonne to Pierre Duhem and those of the Collège de France to Paul Tannery. Today eminent scientists are to be found who openly proclaim their Christian faith and do not consider that it puts any obstacles in the way of their activities as scientific investigators.

Nevertheless these scientists are asking certain questions, as is shown by the following which we quote from a recent book[1] by Louis Leprince-Ringuet, president of the Union Catholique des Scientifiques Français.

> For Christians numerous problems arise in connection with scientific advances and are occupying the minds of both scientific workers and theologians. Is any contact possible between Christ and the pick of this new humanity with its rapid evolution and its exacting scientific standards?
>
> This contact is certainly not easy to establish, or so it would seem; the Christian message is scarcely accepted at all by this new humanity. No doubt there is in the presentation of Christianity, at least under certain forms, aspects which make the approach to it difficult. The vocabulary used is at times somewhat archaic or else the thought is expressed in too rigid and narrow a form. This élite, intelligent, alive and often full of enthusiasm, generally finds no sustenance for its ideal of faith and emancipation in Christianity as it appears to be or as it is offered to them. Christianity, they hold, is surely a belief

[1] L. Leprince-Ringuet, *Des atomes et des hommes* (Paris, 1958).

suited to humanity in an infantile state, a touching and simple-minded point of view, but which the great purifying winds of a more rigorous and positive thought have swept away! And the Church is always suspicious of the progress and evolution of thought. "If she eventually accepts them, it is under duress and by force, and before she does so, she has exhausted all the means of pressure at her command in an effort to oppose the new vision of the universe introduced by science."

Her enemies, both the indifferent and those actively hostile, are only too eager to accuse her of a retrograde, prudent or over-discreet attitude. The choice of adjective requires a close acquaintance with the way science proceeds. A discovery is rarely defined categorically; a scientific truth is, in fact, always partial and subject to revision. Nevertheless, discoveries and new theories are directing science along paths increasingly well-defined and valid. To refuse to take one of these paths prematurely is not necessarily a sign of hostility towards progress. But it is certainly true that some Christians are still prone to be very much on their guard (pp. 168–71).

There is a characteristic example of this persistent attitude of suspicion in some Christians towards science in the Foreword of the review *Dieu Vivant*.[2] I shall quote fairly large excerpts so as to avoid any risk of falsifying the thought of those who wrote it.

In the first place there is a more eirenical confession of faith which explains, although it does not thereby justify, the bitter criticism that follows:

The Church's liturgy sets before the eyes of the faithful an image of the cosmos as it now is in the course of its trans-formation and centred on a transcendent God, its Creator who has so loved men that he became incarnate for their salvation. This cosmos, still showing the traces of original sin, is only the outward and imperfect sign of the world of heaven. Yet within it all creatures need one another and all are called by God. This cosmos is in an ascending movement towards a trans-

[2] Number 7: Éditions du Seuil (Paris, 1945–55).

cendent and glorious harmony; the hope of this consummation ratified by God's promises transforms suffering into a redeeming force and so into a force which brings into being a super-creation (p. 8).

I close the quotation at this point in order to declare at once that Christian scientists, whose vocation is the acquiring of detailed knowledge of the various stages of creation from insentient creatures to those which reason, via all the various grades of living things, nonetheless recognize the transcendence of the supernatural order and the true teleology of the world which they study in all its diversity. One of the most eminent of these men has said so in terms whose clarity and nobility are unsurpassed: "All bodies together, and all minds together, and all their works, are of less worth than the smallest act of charity. Charity is of an infinitely higher order." Pascal was not renouncing his scientific activities when he made this profession of faith, he was insisting on the fact that they were subordinated to a higher task.

While the Christian scientist recognizes that the destiny of the world transcends the knowledge of it which his science brings to him, he cannot allow that his temporal task is essentially vitiated by Promethean pride. And this is precisely the argument put forward in the following passage:

> Science today claims to take the place of the Church and to ensure earthly salvation for mankind. But she has not the means to do this. In the first place, science is no more able to destroy the world than she was able to be present, except in the mind of the angels, when it was created. This is why the fairy garden she attempts to produce to conceal our lost Paradise cannot succeed in putting out of sight an immense and deplorable graveyard whose stones it is unable to remove. Synthetic sugar manufactured at a high temperature by means of the dissipation of energy is not to be compared with the glycogenic function of the liver which renews our bodies, nor to the honey gathered by bees from flowers. Science takes her

stand against the Church as a messenger of life and joy but she can only bring death and despair (p. 8).

I pass over the criticism of beet sugar. We are obviously entitled to prefer honey. It is true that "scientism," now in decline in the intellectual world, still finds recruits in the lower ranks of the scientific professions, but is it just to blame this on the body of scientists as a whole, represented by the word "Science" adorned with a sinister capital? Is it a sign of brotherly love to include Christian scientists as responsible for this state of affairs? To level this accusation against science inevitably leads to this conclusion.

The fact is that the situation of the Christian scientist in the world today is bound to be one of expiatory suffering and anguish. Like Columbus after the discovery of America, he has to prepare toxicants as temporary remedies not to be abused. The Church which continues to teach the Mysteries is speaking to a man pulled in every direction. He shares by faith in a cosmos of plenitude and joy which, in spite of the attacks of Science, remains the true cosmos, but he also works, in the exercise of his intelligence and for most of his daily life, to bring about the existence of a world which denies this cosmos and seeks to destroy it. Is there any Christian scientist, if we reflect seriously, who in his laboratory as he manipulates the most delicate of apparatus, or at his desk as he traces his geometrical and algebraical symbols, has not contributed over the past centuries more or less directly to the manufacture of the atomic bomb? Unconsciously, we admit, since it is only in the twentieth century that the interdependence of the various disciplines and the power of cosmic destruction possessed by Science could be achieved at one and the same time. Although certain optimistic spirits, in their desire to bring about a reconciliation, are trying to persuade us that scientific "truth" is now seen to be quite relative and so no longer has any reason to oppose the Church's dogma, in consequence of which the Christian conscience is not in fact attacked, it is only too obvious in our opinion that Science has only passed in our times beyond the stage of ideological conflict with Christianity in order to embody itself in political and social forms which oppose the Church and wish to destroy her (pp. 12–13).

We duly note the admission of the fact of history—science in our times has passed beyond the stage of ideological conflict with Christianity. This is precisely the reason that led us to alter the title that had been originally chosen for this book. We might well go no further than this admission which, in spite of its context, justifies our own preliminary position. But the twofold objection expressed in the passage just quoted cannot be met with indifference. On the one hand, Science is everywhere put in the dock with its capital S, as apparently in league with Marxism, and on the other hand, the Christian scientist is, so we are told, an accomplice in the use of nuclear energy for military or political ends.

Only one point need be made to reveal the real state of affairs, and that is the anti-Christian character of Marxism and the existence of an authentic persecution of the Church in countries enslaved to the Communist ideology. But the identification of science with Marxism is a quite gratuitous assumption. As for making Christian scientists responsible for the destruction of Hiroshima and Nagasaki, it would be equally arguable and equally unjust to hold that pre-Reformation Catholic theologians were responsible for the massacres that took place during the wars of religion.

And, according to the authors here quoted, it is not even possible as a last resort for the Christian scientist at least to make amends. This also is refused him.

Not that the Christian scientist can or should sever his ties with the modern world and actually break with scientific "knowledge" and the social structures it has evolved. He could not even if he wanted to. He lacks the means just as does the Christian worker who, in our times, would like to escape from toiling in a factory. Further, if he recognizes that he has a vocation to be a scientist, he has not the right, in view of the

high dignity of the world of thought, to withdraw. He ought
even to imprison himself within it just as does the slave who
volunteers to go down into the dark well to bring water to the
surface. This is his way of paying the ransom for original sin
(p. 13).

When they are offered this slave mentality, Christian
scientists are entitled to counter with the words of St Paul:
"we are sons of the free woman, not of the slave; such is the
freedom Christ has won for us".[3]

If we insist on extricating the thesis developed in the pages
just quoted, we see that it may be summed up as the assertion
of an essential duality in the cosmos. On the one hand, there
is the liturgical cosmos, confined to the realm of immediate
sense data, and it is the sign of the presence of God and
contains the pledge of the life to come. Over against it stands
the cosmos studied by the Christian scientist and whose
frontiers he extends by the work of the mind. This second
cosmos has only one aim—to destroy the other. On the
contrary, however, it is the unity of the cosmos which is
asserted throughout the speech made on November 22nd,
1951, by Pius XII at an official reception given to the members of the Pontifical Academy of Science.

The wide range of this speech, and the detailed information
it contains on the most recent data of astrophysics, seem to
show that Pius XII wished to oppose both the accusation of
ignorance of or disdain for science, that is so frequently
levelled at the Church by her adversaries, and also the
tendency (frequently carried, as we have just seen, to considerable lengths) of philosophers and theologians to accen-
tuate the breach between the field of their respective disciplines
and that of the positive sciences.

[3] Gal. 4. 31. St Paul is referring to Abraham's two wives. Agar, the
servant, is the image of the Old Law and Sara, the free woman, of
the New.

In fact, true science, contrary to what was thoughtlessly asserted in the past, increasingly discovers God as its progress advances. It is as though he were lying in wait behind every door that science opens. We mean, too, that the man of science is not the only one to benefit, when he thinks as a philosopher —and how could he do otherwise?—from this progressive knowledge of God which is the fruit of the increase of knowledge, but also all those who share in the new discoveries or turn their attention to them. This is especially true of genuine philosophers who will profit by them since, taking scientific achievements as the basis of their own rational speculations, they establish their own conclusions more securely, find a clearer light with which to dispel any future shadows and more convincing arguments to help them to offer an increasingly satisfactory answer to difficulties and objections.

Less than a year after this speech, on September 7th, 1952, Pius XII received in audience 650 members of the Eighth General Assembly of the International Astronomical Union, which was held that year in Rome. He delivered a speech to them in French and it is no less important than the preceding one. Once more we note his anxiety to obtain exact information and the expression of his sincere admiration for the work of investigation carried out by the human mind.

When we stand before the picture of the cosmos we have merely roughly sketched above, and which is the fruit of the long and laborious researches not of one man but of whole generations of investigators belonging to many different nations, it is not only the gigantic mass of the whole and of its parts or the harmony of their movements which so profoundly impresses us, but also the work of man's inquiring mind as he discovers such a vast panorama. Linked by nature to physical conditions whose dimensions are so minute, the human mind has succeeded in grasping to itself the immensity of the universe and has transcended all the vistas which alone, at first sight, the feeble power of his senses seemed able to offer him.

The pope then asked whether the progress of human research could penetrate the ultimate mysteries of the universe.

The answer given by powerful minds who have gone most deeply into the secrets of the cosmos is very cautious and unpretentious. We are, so they think, only at the beginning. Much ground remains to be covered and will be covered without fail. Nevertheless, it is not at all probable that even the genius of the greatest investigator will ever be able to solve all the riddles of the physical universe, for they postulate and point to the existence of a Mind infinitely superior, the Divine Mind, which creates, preserves, governs and hence knows and scrutinizes in one supreme intuition, today as it did at the dawn of the first day of creation, all that exists: "And the spirit of God moved over the waters."

We now know what the Apostolic See thinks about a so-called opposition between the liturgical cosmos and the cosmos studied by science, and the view that the latter erects a barrier against the divine presence, that the enlarging of its field of vision by technical instruments attenuates the transparency of the universe before the eyes of the believer. The fact is that it increases it.

Once we have rid ourselves of the false problem of any hostility towards science on the part of Christianity, we find genuine problems arising, and they are connected with Pascal's distinction between the three orders; the order of matter, of mind, and of supernatural charity. Once we have recognized their heterogeneousness, then the superiority of the second over the first and still more of the third over the two others, we are beset with the temptation to absorb the first in the second, or to cast both of them aside and to rise to the third. Thus we arrive in philosophy at idealism, in theology at Docetism and moralism. But, if we do this, we are emptying the mystery of the Incarnation of its meaning, for we are refusing to accept, in all their realism and fullness, the words of St John: "The Word became flesh."

The scale of values is respected not by way of negation but by way of submission: the submission of matter to mind practised by the scientist controlling his experiment in his anxiety to verify his hypothesis, the submission of the mind to the mysterious action of grace to which Pascal's *Mémorial* bears witness. This twofold submission remains throughout life difficult to practise. For most of the time it is only possible by means of alternating periods of application to routine tasks and to the work of reflection, to tasks that are solely human and to a secret call upon the divine assistance. This inevitable swing to and fro in our existence is encouraged by the alternation of day and night and by the periodical return each week of the Lord's Day.

Yet it is very desirable that there should be established, in time and in proportion to our loyal observance of periods of recollection, what Maurice Nédoncelle very aptly calls "an osmosis ... which ... enriches nature little by little with the revelation of supernature".[4]

Evidence that this osmosis of scientist and believer is possible is provided in the writings of two men of science who have died only recently, Pierre Termier and Fr Teilhard de Chardin. Louis Leprince-Ringuet recalls the figure of Termier as follows:

> I remember hearing Termier at one of the annual meetings of the five academies. This dignified man with his serious air, his broad and shining head, rose when his turn came after the representatives of the moral sciences and of the academy of inscriptions, and began to sing the praises of "the joy of knowledge". It was as though a light had suddenly burst upon us, dazzling us all, an immense and fascinating ray, dimming to nothing the little candles more or less well lit by his colleagues, including even the representative of the Académie Française. When all was over and the speeches of the five delegates were finished, the great poem outlined by Termier

[4] *Is there a Christian Philosophy?* p. 142. English translation by Dom Illtyd Trethowan. Volume 10 in this series.

alone remained in our minds. I was a student at the time and it is probable that, although I did not realize it, this light remained in my own mind illuminating the path I was to follow.[5]

The book which opens with the speech on "the joy of knowledge" ends with Pierre Termier's personal witness to the Christian faith. It runs to 24 pages and several of them describe a stage in our knowledge which is now outdated. Here are the last two pages:

> For my part, I cannot survey from even a slightly higher vantage point the history of the Earth, the history geology unrolls before my eyes, without finding the idea of a God who is not only a Creator but also the Providence governing the world, quite natural and almost necessary. The slow fashioning of the planet leading, it would seem, to the creation of life; the gradual development of life in accordance with a perfectly defined and determined plan leading, it would seem, to the crowning splendour of the creation of man gifted with reason and freedom; the vegetable and animal kingdom taking possession of the surface of the globe and, in a sense, preparing it for man to live upon; then the beginning of the kingdom of thought, and the Earth gradually conquered by man and becoming that unimaginable reality, a dwelling-place for souls more or less gifted with consciousness, aware of their own immaterial nature, of their almost divine dignity and their immortality: it is of this that I am constantly reminded by the sight of mountains and abysses, by meditation on the passing of innumerable centuries, by the spectacle of the vicissitudes through which the Earth has passed. Doubtless, this is not sufficient to make Christianity necessary but, for a man in possession of the Christian faith, how it encourages him to adhere to it with all his strength!
>
> Science, and I mean the corpus of all the sciences, is in my view like one of those vast and magnificent cathedrals which the Middle Ages scattered in such profusion throughout this land of France. Those who drew up their plans and laid their foundations were believers. They were followed by other men

[5] Louis Leprince-Ringuet, *Des atomes et des hommes*, p. 153.

who did not have the same faith or the same love; and among those who are still putting the finishing touches to their decoration in our own day or who repair the damage wrought by time in these sublime buildings, many have no knowledge of the profound meaning of these poems in stone glorifying Christ, his Mother and his saints. But a gentle yet powerful influence emanates from the blackened vaults, the lofty stained glass windows with their strange colours, the rose-windows touched with flame by the setting sun. The visitor casually enters, sometimes with a mocking smile on his lips. Gradually, in the silent and shadowy aisles, serious thoughts steal into the mind. The soul of the believer and the soul of the unbeliever are both deeply moved. The believer is encouraged to believe, hope and love still more. The unbeliever finds himself doubting his very doubts and his soul trembles at the question—is it not God himself who has just spoken to me?[6]

The same alliance between rigorous scientific thought and the delight of the poet, together with the soaring soul of the mystic for whom creation is God's transparent veil, is found in Fr Teilhard de Chardin and expressed with a lyricism similar to that of Pierre Termier. For both men, their work as geologists developed in them an admiration, almost an affection for the Earth (note the use of the capital letter every time the word is used in the passage quoted above). How many pages in the published work of de Chardin could also be grouped together to form an anthology "in praise of the Earth", or a hymn chanting "the joy of knowledge"!

Yet we prefer his travel letters, because they are faithful and day-to-day witnesses to this mutual impenetration of knowledge and thought and of thought and mysticism in his soul. Here are a few extracts:

Off the coast of the Sinai Peninsula, April 15th, 1923.

As the sun was disappearing from sight in a diminutive eddy of fiery clouds, the mountains of Egypt, till then shrouded in

[6] P. Termier, *La joie de connaître* (Paris, 1926), pp. 332-3.

mist, began to show every hue of violet from the deepest to the most transparent and mauve. A long line of pointed, serrated peaks silhouetted against the golden sky at length alone remained visible. Yet all this magical scene was nothing in comparison with what the mind discovered in these territories that are almost unknown, which almost no one visits and where, perhaps for that very reason, the most mysterious phases of our religious history have their roots. I should have liked to land on these rocky coasts, not only to test them with my hammer, but to listen also for the voice from the Burning Bush. Yet surely the time has passed when God spoke in the desert. We now understand that "He who is" does not make his voice heard in this place or that, for the summits on which he dwells are not those of an inaccessible mountain, but are in a far deeper realm of reality. The secret of the world lies wherever we succeed in seeing the transparency of the Universe.

During an expedition to China, August 26th, 1923.

Somewhat too absorbed as I am by Science to be able to philosophize a great deal, although I am increasingly convinced as I enter into my own soul that the Knowledge of Christ in every sphere, the true mystical knowledge, is the only one that counts, I find myself entirely committed when I return to my work as a geologist. Yet the slightest reflection shows me perfectly clearly that this task (and it is for me a vital necessity in so far as it is part of the whole impulse of my life) ceases to have any definitive interest in itself. Gradually and with increasing success, I work out, as I pray, my "Mass on the altar of material things" (this later became: "the Mass on the altar of the World", *La Messe sur le Monde*).

During field work in the Dalai-Nord area, June 11th, 1927.

Since I am so involved in my geological work and also because of a feeling of weariness arising from uncertainty regarding my possible course of action in the future, I do less thinking perhaps this year than I did on my former journeys. I am still most active when I say my "Mass on the altar of the World" to make each new day divine.

The editor then quotes two paragraphs from the following unpublished passage:

> Once more, Lord, not in the forests of Aisne, but in the steppes of Asia, I am without bread, wine and altar. Therefore I pass beyond symbols to the pure majesty of the Real and I, your priest, shall offer to you on the altar of the whole Earth, the labour and sorrow of the World...
>
> Accept, O Lord, this whole host which creation, drawn as it is towards you, offers to you at the dawn of this new day. Bread, which is our toil, is in itself, I know, only an immense process of disintegration. The wine, which is our pain, is no more, alas, than a beverage in a state of dissolution. Yet at the heart of this formless mass you have set an irresistible and sanctifying desire which makes us all, the unbeliever and the believer, cry out: "O Lord, make us all one!"[7]

The ardent desire for unity, which brings this prayer to an end, is perhaps the best definition of Fr Teilhard de Chardin's programme of life and thought. None of the values of this world, not even those most submerged in the realm of matter, are to be annihilated, they are rather to be taken up into our union with the person of Christ who first assumed them into his own human nature but yet without sacrificing anything of his divine nature or of the share in it that is granted by grace to the Christian.

Although it may be possible to reach a degree of union with God in such a way that human values, far from raising obstacles, are themselves genuinely raised to a higher status, yet it is more difficult to prove that Christianity not only does not mutilate human values, but demands the full evolution of humanity in this world, and hence that the establishment of the kingdom of God on earth has an interest in the progress of scientific knowledge and its application to the process by

[7] Teilhard de Chardin, *Lettres de voyage* (1923–39), edited by Claude Aragonnès (Paris, 1956), pp. 26–46, 105.

which the material world is transformed for the benefit or the increased welfare of its inhabitants.

This was the standpoint of Fr Teilhard de Chardin in his various writings, and he has therefore been reproached for not taking sufficient account of the fact that, since original sin, the material world has become a source of temptation for the spiritual man.

We can call on a professional theologian, whose early death is to be lamented, Fr de Montcheuil, to point out a *via media* between these two opposing themes: the theme of essential and inevitable conflict, and the theme of a pre-arranged harmony, unfolding itself in the process of time, between Christianity and human values.

> This is a question which, in one form or another, many are now asking themselves. Is there not, it is urged, a mutual incompatibility between humanism with its passionate love of all things human, and Christianity the religion of detachment, of preference accorded to God or rather to the exclusive love of God? Is not conflict inevitable? This is the question put to us, or rather, quite often it is changed to a statement of fact. It is the apparent truth of this statement which provides some of the more serious arguments of anti-Christian polemics with their cogency.
>
> Catholics obviously deny its truth, but we are bound to admit that their explicit answers are not always very satisfactory. Many of them go to the opposite extreme in their attack on anti-Christian humanism and what they say is substantially as follows: "Far from contradicting and stifling humanism, Christianity on the contrary brings it into effect; it alone, in fact, does so. There is no conflict at all between them; they are in entire agreement. To be a Christian is the only way to be fully human. The Christian religion takes human nature into itself and raises it to a higher plane."
>
> It goes without saying that I do not agree that there is any inescapable and definitive opposition between Christianity and humanism. Nor do I admit the validity of the terms of the

objection as put forward at the beginning of this section. Yet the answer I have just summarized does not satisfy me. Such a Christian humanism is too facile . . . although there is a genuine and fundamental agreement between humanism and Christianity, it is necessary that conflict should arise between them. Agreement cannot be achieved in the field of truth without a conflict that has been surmounted.

Here are the two statements between which the conflict arises.

God, if he is God, stands forth as he who cannot be related to anything else, he who cannot be allotted a subordinate rôle in any sphere whatsoever. To claim that this is possible is to deny him. Above all, he demands our all. . . .

It is therefore not possible just to say: "I love God and humanity." By claiming I do both, am I not, by the same token, refusing God that exclusive love which he not only in fact requires but which his very existence demands?

Can we then say: "I love humanity for God's sake"?

To love humanity for God's sake, means that I love it neither for my own sake because to possess it would make me supremely happy, nor for its own sake because its values are rooted in what it actually is. No, it means that I love humanity simply because its existence corresponds to certain mysterious purposes of God's, and I love it solely by virtue of these purposes. This means that I treat humanity as a means to an end. I am not making it the object of my love at all, but merely an opportunity for my love of God. And is this worthy of humanity?

Conflict therefore seems inevitable and an act of renunciation is essential.

This love for humanity within us, this desire we feel to develop it and to be one with it, to grow with it and to take into ourselves its vast resources and to live its great adventure, all this is no mere accidental or superficial wish. It springs from our very nature. When therefore God makes himself known to us and offers himself to our love, he demands of us an act of total renunciation reaching down to the deepest levels of our being. We cannot do better than compare it to death itself.

We may note in passing that this comparison is found in the Gospel. The grain of wheat is buried in the earth. This reference clarifies what now follows:

> Our acceptance of this death is accomplished in the act of faith. If this death was destined to leave us in the situation in which we were before the act of faith, there would be a radical and final divorce between the divine and the human, God's demands would be our ruin ... but, in fact, this death is no more than a transition ... we have been born again, we have entered a new universe. ...
>
> By the fact of the Incarnation, the whole of human nature has already an initial link with the Word of God made flesh. Human nature belongs to the Word and is destined for the Word. Even before we as individuals make the act of faith which is to give us effective membership in Christ, the human race is one in Christ with the Godhead. All that leads to the evolution of humanity, all that perfects humanity in the line of its own characteristics, all that enlarges its resources, is then, in a sense, for the sake of Jesus Christ himself. ... This is why, in the context of our Christian faith, and in the vistas opened up before us by this faith, we can give our love to humanity without refusing anything whatsoever to God. ... This is why our faith overcomes the contradiction: "This is the victory, our faith."

This mystery of death and life, realized in the first place in the person of Christ during his passage through this world, must be realized by each individual Christian in his turn. He has to live it progressively since he can only live it imperfectly.

> Each of us must follow the call from on high and accept death by passing through this absolute detachment in the night of the spirit. We cannot come into true contact with humanity in its depths unless we have had the courage to renounce it as we have renounced ourselves. Our renouncement, at the moment when we accept it, is bound to appear utter and

final . . . every forward step we make in our love for humanity must be accompanied at once by a forward step in this renóuncement which gives us the right to love and places in our hands—yet with so great a difference—the very reality we have just renounced.[8]

We must accept such detachment not in the spirit of slaves but in the gladness and joy of Easter. Fr Teilhard de Chardin, whose radical optimism has been criticized, willingly consented to make many renunciations during his lifetime and they led him to his most fruitful ventures and doubtless were needed so that his life and work might have a wider influence. We should not forget that he wanted to die on Easter Day and that God granted him his wish.

The plan of this book is already clear from the series of passages just quoted, just as the design of a stained-glass window appears when its many-coloured pieces are assembled together.

I have now to give my work the form of a personal reflection which I offer as such to Christian scientists. The book is addressed to them in the first place, but also to all believers and, in a more general way, to all minds with a sense of spiritual values.

In Part I I shall bring forward one after the other three fundamental aspects of Christianity. As we pass from one to the other, the mind of the reader will be led towards the answer I hope to give to the question implied in this book's title. Part II will recall the historical circumstances in which Christians and scientists in the past have thought they could find a meeting-ground for their belief and the sciences of nature. Part III will be devoted to present-day problems, especially to those which face an élite among Christian

[8] These quotations are from Fr de Montcheuil's lecture on "Humanisme et Christianisme", the concluding section of the book entitled *Le royaume et ses exigences* (Paris, 1957), pp. 102–16.

scientists in their anxiety to achieve an osmosis—and it is not easy to achieve—between their faith and their professional tasks.

My plan, therefore, does not include an examination of the classic objections raised against the Christian religion on scientific grounds by unbelievers. The reader will find a methodical account of these together with a detailed refutation in another book published in this series.

PART I

SOME ASPECTS OF CHRISTIANITY

CHAPTER I

THE ONE THING NECESSARY

"Thy kingdom come." This prayer is at the centre of those requests in the Lord's Prayer that do not directly concern ourselves. Our Lord himself taught it to his disciples and it is the echo of his own prayer, but with one difference. As a loving and submissive Son, Christ asked that the kingdom of his Father should be established on earth as it is in heaven. We, who have come into existence since the Son has returned to the Father and shared his kingship, "sitting at his right hand", desire to see the coming upon earth of the kingdom of the Father and the Son. It would doubtless be preferable to say "of the Father *through* the Son", for it is in proportion as the kingship of Christ, sent by the Father, is recognized and fully accepted by men that God's sovereignty will be established on earth and those false gods abolished in whose name man claims to make himself the master of the world.

The coming of the kingdom of God is the central point of history, a history scarred with sin, yet inspired from the beginning with a lasting hope in the coming of a redeemer. The birth of the Messias, the son of David, prophesied dimly in figure and prepared by the rise in Israel of a theocratic monarchy, is the bringing into being of an initial coming of God's kingdom. "Repent (that is, change your way of thinking and acting), the kingdom of heaven is at hand." This is the central theme of Christ's preaching and it was already present in that of the Forerunner. It was given to the apostles as their watchword when they were sent out on their mission.

Yet during his own ministry, Jesus did not claim the inheritance of this kingship. The idea of his kingship was wrapped in too much obscurity. Covetous desires in abundance urged the multitude, fed by a miracle, to offer him the crown. Even the apostles themselves were not free from the ambition to secure the best places in the kingdom. But when he is led in chains before Pilate and questioned by him before the gaze of a riotous crowd, when no misunderstanding is any longer possible, Jesus does not hesitate to proclaim himself a king. He only makes it clear that his kingdom "is not of this world". It is on the Cross that his kingship from beyond this world is recognized for the first time, and that by a repentant sinner, for whom this kingship is the only hope left: "Lord, remember me when thou comest into thy kingdom." We know how this hope was fulfilled: "this day thou shalt be with me in Paradise."

The kingdom, the final hope at the hour of death, is already the most desirable of life's possessions. It gives life its value and justifies the conquering activities of man: "The kingdom of heaven is like a treasure hidden in a field; a man has found it and hidden it again, and now, for the joy it gives him, is going home to sell all that he has and buy that field. Again, the kingdom is as if a trader were looking for rare pearls: and now he has found one pearl of great cost, and has sold all that he had and bought it" (Matt. 13. 44–6).

It has a unique value, its discovery brings joy, we are anxious to sacrifice everything to possess the object of our desires, these are the characteristics of the kingdom. They explain the demands Christ set before those who were candidates for the apostolate. Since they were more frequently with him during his wandering life, they would have to renounce the pleasures of home life and the security guaranteed by wealth. In a word, every risk had to be taken if they were to share in the kingdom. This is why, if Christianity were not true, Christians would be, as St Paul wrote, "the most miserable of men".

Yet, once we have entered the kingdom, we recover all we have consented to lose in order to cross its threshold. We recover our own selves, but without any self-centred egoism or any satisfaction for our possessive instincts. Christ has promised us this: "Seek ye first the kingdom of God and the rest shall be added unto you." This is not to be "in addition" as the above translation suggests, but for the sake of the kingdom and its extension. The kingdom is "the one thing necessary", the rest is God's gift and is destined to advance the kingdom.

The expression "kingdom of God" familiar to the first three Evangelists is almost entirely absent from St John's Gospel. This is because during the first century of her history the Church grew in numbers and the Christian converts from paganism were now more numerous than those from Judaism. For the pagans the concept of a kingship of God in this world or exercised in his name awakened no familiar memory from their own history. For the Christians of Jewish origin, the ruin of Jerusalem and the destruction of the Temple had opened their eyes to the final cleavage between the Old and the New Covenants. Other themes took the place of the idea of the kingdom or else served as a complement to it. Those most familiar to St John were "life" and "light", and the first led to the second, since "the life was the light of men" (John 1. 4).

John, the beloved disciple, is the last witness of this life whose source is in God and which was made manifest in Jesus Christ. John's own life was providentially prolonged so that the proclamation of Christ's "life" might resound throughout the first Christian generations: "Yes, life dawned; and it is as eye-witnesses that we give you news of that life, that eternal life, which ever abode with the Father and has dawned, now, on us" (1 John 1. 2). It is not surprising therefore that John should have preserved, in preference to his Master's preaching of the kingdom, the words in which he proclaimed from the beginning of his apostolic life that he was the source of life for men: "The man who drinks the water I give him," said Christ to a woman of Samaria at Jacob's well, "will not know thirst any more. The water I give him, will be a spring of water within him, that flows continually to bring him ever-lasting life" (John 4. 13–14). The most solemn and enlightening of Jesus' declarations is that with which he began his high-priestly prayer on the eve of his death: "Father, the time has come; give glory now to thy Son, that thy Son may give glory to thee. Thou hast put him in authority over all mankind, to bring eternal life to all those thou hast entrusted to him. Eternal life is knowing thee, who art the only true God, and Jesus Christ, whom thou has sent" (John 17).

It is not specifically stated that this life is exclusively that which will make us blessed throughout eternity. The word "eternal" essentially means that this life flowers in us *over and above*, beyond our mortal life. This "beyond" refers in the first place to our nature and so makes possible and necessary a life *"beyond" time*. Eternal is here a synonym for *supernatural*.

The knowledge of God and of Christ in which already in this life our supernatural life consists, is neither exclusively nor even principally of an intellectual nature. It has rather to be understood, and St John's Gospel suggests this in a great many passages, as a familiar relationship: "I know mine and mine know me" (John 10. 14). It is quite compatible with an active life in the service of our brother men. This osmosis of Christ's life and our own, together with all its ins-and-outs and all its adventures, is admirably illustrated in the apostolic career of St Paul. The Apostle was not writing from an exclusively personal point of view when he told the Galatians: "And yet I am alive; or rather not I; it is Christ that lives in me" (Gal. 2. 20). The argument which is developed in the context of this sentence requires that "I" should indicate not St Paul in person, but the Christian as such.

There is still more to be said. Not only Christians but all men are called to share this intimate knowledge of Christ and his Father; they are invited to live this family life which is that of God himself: "I have other sheep, too, which do not belong to this fold: I must bring them in too; they will listen to my voice; so there will be one fold and one shepherd" (John 10. 16). Thus the theme of "life" meets the theme of the kingdom in the social reality of the Church which is open to all men. Sheep and subjects are one and the same. Like David his ancestor, Christ is both King and Shepherd.

Like the kingdom, whose inner aspect it expresses in the individual conscience, life in Christ is "the only thing necessary". Whoever possesses it, possesses all things. In comparison with this All, the rest is only of value in so far as it shares this life. If we attempt to isolate it from the All, it has to be counted as nothing.

This explains why, without denying any human values, the believer can greet death as a deliverance from all that limits and delays in him the full flowering of the life of Christ. Fortified by the promise of our Lord whose resurrection on Easter morning is the foreshadowing of his own on the day of the Parousia, every Christian can and should make his own the words of St Paul: "For me, life means Christ: death is a prize to be won" (Phil. 1. 21).

CHAPTER II

THE LAW OF WORK ACCORDING TO CHRIST AND ST PAUL

The Gospel says of John the Baptist that "he dwelt in the wilderness until the day when he was made manifest to Israel" (Luke 1. 80). His way of life in the desert is described in picturesque terms: "And he John wore a garment of camel's hair, and a leather girdle about his loins: and locusts and wild honey were his food" (Matt. 3. 4).

Flight into the desert was exceedingly popular in the fourth century. The first hermits, Paul and Antony, owe their fame to it. Their example, together with a child's voice as the messenger of God's call, helped to produce the sudden shock which freed Augustine from the bonds of the flesh. Jerome plunged into the desert to quell the fires of passion and, though with less success, to master his irascible temperament. The solitaries of the desert lived a contemplative life centred around the one thing necessary. The cenobites wished to build in the desert a miniature image of the kingdom of God.

Jesus did not choose this path when he reached the age at which the young man, emerging from the chrysalis of childhood, looks beyond the familiar horizons to discover his own personal way of life. Not that Jesus lacked initiative; his flight at the age of twelve shows that he was completely free in regard to his parents and already resolved to fulfil the mission he had received from his Father.

The return to Nazareth with Mary and Joseph, adolescence following childhood without any break, the apprenticeship to his father's trade, his taking over of the family business after Joseph's death, with the many ties of a life led in the service of others, all are the result of completely voluntary decisions, full of meaning for anyone who is willing to reflect upon them.

Not only did Christ not escape from the environment and the trade into which he had been born, but this environment and this trade were, we believe, determined by him in an eternal decree when "in the beginning was the Word, and the Word was with God". This is doubtless a lesson in humility, but Jesus did not go down to the lowest grades in the social scale, he was not a "bearer of burdens" not at least until the day when he took the Cross upon his shoulders and on this Cross bore the crushing burden of the world's sins.

The work of a village artisan is not confined to manual labour, to the mechanical repetition of movements that have been learned once and for all. It demands a daily adaptation to the various needs and wishes of his customers. It pre-supposes the acquired knowledge of the techniques taught by the master to the apprentice, but it also requires a judicious choice of those which are best suited to resolve the problem with which he is actually faced. It is true, as Pascal says, that Jesus Christ "made no inventions", that is, he did not forestall the improvements introduced at a later date in the practice of his trade. The reason is not far to seek. The reality of the incarnation of the Son of God, which was to have doubt thrown upon it by the Docetists, would be seen as all the more certain in that the Son of Man was faithful to the law of time, the law St Luke threw into relief on two occasions in his narrative of Christ's childhood. Any invention, since it would have been a leap forward in time, would have weakened the

impression of actuality which was made upon his contemporaries by the way Jesus of Nazareth lived and acted.
This does not exclude the likelihood that he showed ingenuity
in the carrying out of his various jobs, for this is the quality
which distinguishes the work of the artisan from that of the
assembly line. This then was the life Christ lived until he was
thirty.

The same preference for a practical trade through which
the Son of God decided to enter into daily contact with the
humanity which he had come to save, and to become socially
one with it, reappears in his choice of collaborators. All or
almost all of those he gathered round him in his apostolic
ministry were craftsmen.

After preparing himself for this new and final stage in his
brief career on earth by a period of forty days in the desert—
he did not despise asceticism but subordinated it to a higher
end—we see Jesus following in the wake of John the Baptist
and recruiting from among the latter's disciples the first of
his apostles, Andrew and Peter, James and John, two groups
united by the ties of brotherhood and the same open-air
occupation requiring mutual assistance and self-sacrifice. The
circumstances in which, on the shores of the Lake of Galilee,
they abandoned their trade of fishermen in order to take part
in the preaching of the kingdom, shows that, unbeknown to
them, their arduous task had prepared them for their new
vocation. The nets filled to bursting point, which they brought
to shore, prefigured the miraculous draughts of believers
brought into the infant Church. On that very day, Jesus
assured Peter that this would be so: "Henceforth thou shalt
catch men."

Yet a day came when Peter returned to his nets, a day when,
after another night of fruitless toil, a voice from the shore invited him to cast down his nets once more and a new
miraculous draught showed that Peter's loyalty to his craft
was pleasing to his risen Master. The ultimate meaning of the

miracle was the re-affirmation of Peter's apostolic mission and his prerogatives as leader. The full nets foretold the Church and the day was nigh when the reality would take the place of the figure.

These episodes, the most familiar and significant in the Gospel narratives, show us how Jesus excelled in providing spiritual realities with a material outward covering borrowed from the social and work life of his times. The teaching by parables on the shores of the lake—with the fisherman's boat as the preacher's pulpit—offered still wider scope for illustrations taken from many different kinds of trades in order to produce symbols whose meaning was grasped by the hearers according as their dispositions varied. The souls of men of good will were enlightened, while those who were not in a fit state to understand remained in a merciful cloud of unawareness.

One by one they go by—the sower and the reaper, the unemployed waiting for someone to give them work, the owner of the vineyard who has built a watchtower so that he may keep an eye on the grape-gatherers and drive away marauders. If the property is considerable and involves various kinds of cultivations, a steward is essential and he signs contracts and collects the money from sales. Sometimes he is a rogue; sin is not absent from the world on which Jesus looked. The steward's dishonest behaviour, however, suggests a lesson in prudence on which the sons of light would do well to reflect. There is even an occasion when we are told of the conduct of an iniquitous judge and then recommended to persevere in our prayer to God.

But for the most part, God is shown under the image of the "Master of the house," the father of the family anxious to feed and protect his children, the far-seeing and generous employer giving credit to his active and devoted servants and granting them a kingly reward. It is true that he severely punishes idleness and hardness of heart, but he offers a merciful and loving welcome to the prodigal son when he returns home.

For his own self-portrait Christ turned to the work of the shepherd. He described it lovingly and ennobled it. It was a familiar image in Israel and occurs over and over again in the psalms in praise of the Providence of God as manifested towards his people during the course of history. The image becomes a personal one in the Gospel teaching. The "good shepherd", that is, the most worthy representative of his craft, is he who knows each of his sheep and who is troubled as soon as any single one of them is in danger of being lost. To defend them, he goes to meet danger from wild beasts and robbers; he is ready to lay down his life for their sakes.

It is not surprising then that it was not far from a group of shepherds, kept awake by the cares of their calling on a cold night, that Jesus chose to be born, nor that these shepherds, when they had been told of his birth by the voices of the angels, should have been the first to adore him.

In men's judgement, there are no silly trades, but as a proverb adds, only silly people. In the judgement of God, there is no trade under a curse, there are only sinful ways of behaving, for example, the conduct of Judas and of those who behave as he did when they deliver over to Satan the living Christ in a soul in a state of innocence, either their own or that of someone else, especially a child's.

There is therefore no contradiction between the practice of any trade, whatever its technique, and a life devoted to the one thing necessary, to know God and him whom he has sent, Jesus Christ. We must go even further; these two tasks together make up the normal life of the Christian. This was both the teaching and the practice of St Paul and in this he followed the example of the carpenter of Nazareth.

It is noteworthy that the apostle who searched most deeply into the mystery of Christ, and who received from him the mission of revealing it to his brethren, never took advantage of this mission to live at anybody's expense. He wrote as follows to the Thessalonians:

> We would not even be indebted to you for our daily bread, we earned it in weariness and toil, working with our hands, night and day, so as not to be a burden to any of you; not that we are obliged to do so, but as a model for your own behaviour; you were to follow our example. The charge we gave you on our visit was that the man who refuses to work must be left to starve. And now we are told that there are those among you who live in idleness, neglecting their own business to mind other people's. We charge all such, we appeal to them in the Lord Jesus Christ, to earn their bread by going on calmly with their work. (2 Thess. 3. 8–12.)

St Luke's account of Paul's arrival at Corinth tells us about the trade by means of which he earned his own living:

> After these things, departing from Athens, he came to Corinth. And finding a certain Jew, named Aquila, born in Pontus, lately come from Italy, with Priscilla his wife (because that Claudius had commanded all Jews to depart from Rome) he came to them. And because he was of the same trade, he remained with them and wrought (now they were tent-makers by trade). (Acts 18. 1–3, Douay.)

When Paul left Corinth for Ephesus, Aquila and Priscilla accompanied him and set up their workshop in this city, while Paul went on towards Antioch and passed through Galatia and Phrygia. On his return to Ephesus and during the three years he remained there, St Paul plied with them his trade as a tent-maker. When, therefore, he made up his mind to go up to Jerusalem, where he knew that he was to be put into chains for Christ's sake, he was able to tell the elders of the church of Ephesus whom he had invited to meet him at Miletus, as he showed them his calloused hands: "You yourselves know: for such things as were needful for me and them that are with me, these hands have furnished. I have shewed you all things, how that so labouring you ought to support the weak, and to remember the word of the Lord Jesus, how he said: It is a more blessed thing to give rather than to receive."

It was at Tarsus, his native city, that in his youth Paul had learned the craft of tent-making. Cilicia, a country of high mountains and pasture-lands, was renowned for its huge herds of long-haired goats. Goat or camel hair was used for weaving the rough canvas which, long before it provided hair-shirts (*cilices*) for ascetics, was used by the wandering shepherds and the soldiers as material for their tents, since it has a two-fold advantage: it is both strong and waterproof. It is easy enough to imagine St Paul, at such times as he was not making his triumphant speeches in the Ephesus synagogue or giving instruction to his converts in the school of a man named Tyrannos, receiving in the workshop of his fellow labourers all those who were anxious to acquire a more profound knowledge of Christ's doctrine.

Already, while St Paul had been away from the town, a learned Alexandrine Jew, named Apollo, who was soon to become his rival in the apostolate, had come to this workshop to receive from the humble weavers a further course of religious instruction with a view to Christian baptism; hitherto he had known only the baptism of John the Baptist.

On his return Paul resumed both his manual work and his long spiritual conversations with the most fervent of his disciples. To the rhythm of human work, of the continual backward and forward movement of the shuttle between the two rows of the odd and even threads of the series, another and divine work was in progress under the inspiration of the Spirit. The mystery of Christ, sent by the Father and who had reconciled all men through his blood and had then been raised up to the right hand of God, receiving the primacy over the whole universe of things and persons, the mystery of the Christ who had chosen Paul as his herald among the pagans so that they might share in an order of truth hitherto reserved for the chosen people, this mystery was now at long last proclaimed and was slowly making its way into the minds of men ready to receive it; at the same time it was woven into the fabric of everyday life.

CHAPTER III

THE UNIVERSAL
CHARACTER OF
PENTECOST

The mystery of the Incarnation of the Son of God is the mystery of the entry into time of an eternal Person and is so described in the Prologue to the fourth Gospel. Born of the Father in an eternal "present", the Son was sent by him into the world at a given moment in history, at this moment and at no other because mankind is not a procession of interchangeable individuals, a never-ending cycle that can only be intersected in a purely arbitrary fashion. From its beginnings mankind has slowly ascended towards maturity, towards the possibility of a more interior life, and also towards a greater diffusion of its various ideas. Greek wisdom, from which one of the books of the Bible drew its inspiration, the rule of Rome furrowing the territories annexed to the Empire with its vast network of roads, and the renewal of Jewish piety after the return from the Exile, all these factors combined to produce that *sacra plenitudo temporis*, planned by Providence for the first advent of the kingdom of God.

Since the Father had chosen this period, Jesus accepted as an obedient Son the consequences of this choice. *He was a man of his time.* Since he belonged to God's chosen people, he accepted its most trivial customs and its most exacting prescriptions. Hence, he was circumcised on the eighth day after his birth, he was presented and redeemed in the Temple, he observed the feasts of the calendar and the prohibitions concerning food. He himself said of these ordinances: "I have come not to destroy but to fulfil." He fulfilled them in the first place by faithfully observing them, but in a more profound way by giving them in his own person their ultimate meaning, and thus prepared for their early and final abolition, unaware of the fact though his fellow countrymen were. Hence he was the *Lamb of God* who by his own sacrifice was to make the slaughter of sheep in their thousands no longer necessary.

This faithful observance, which reached its climax at the moment when the veil of the Temple was torn from top to bottom, gives the Gospel its local colour and its sense of period. All its narrative is typical of a given country and a given time. So much so that it is impossible for us to have a genuine knowledge of Christ if we do not see him *here and now* in the context in which he chose to live. He himself had no desire deliberately to pass beyond its frontiers and only did so accidentally. His harsh reply to the Canaanite woman who had begged him to heal her daughter, sounds strange to us: "My errand is only to the lost sheep of the house of Israel. . . . It is not right to take the children's bread and throw it to the dogs." It is true that when he spoke these words, Jesus knew they would cause an upsurge of trust and faith in the soul of the woman who was asking a favour of him. He already had every intention of healing her daughter. But there are other sayings of Christ which confirm that during his mortal life his immediate field of activity was strictly limited: "Do not go into the walks of the Gentiles, or enter into any city of Samaria", was his instruction to the apostles when he first sent them out to preach.

Yet we are not contradicting ourselves when we say that although an understanding of Christ's teaching requires a knowledge of the history of Israel and of the conditions of life in Palestine at the beginning of the Christian era, the scope of this teaching is universal. In the lifetime of Jesus his method of teaching, when compared to that of the scribes and the doctors of the Law, was clearly entirely new to his immediate hearers and this was one of the causes of the openly declared hostility of the official representatives of the Jewish religion. He did not belittle the ancient Covenant but declared that the kingdom of God is open to all men. The parable of the banquet prepared for invited guests who refused to come, and so were replaced by passers-by from the streets, is even more significant. Christ's conversation with the Samaritan woman interprets it for us. God seeks worshippers "in spirit and in truth". He will find them over the whole earth and the days of the Temple of Jerusalem are numbered.

A profound saying of St Peter's gives a clear impression of the universal vision the apostles acquired as a result of Christ's preaching. When several of his disciples left him because they balked at his mysterious prophecy of the Eucharist, Jesus turned to the Twelve and said: "Would you, too, go away?" Peter speaking on behalf of them all, exclaimed: "Lord, to whom should we go? Thy words are the words of eternal life."

Peter and his companions nevertheless remained very attached to their earthly country and to the hope that they would see the risen Christ in control of its future destiny. This hope is revealed in the question they put to Jesus on the very day he was to take leave of this world: "Lord, dost thou mean to restore the dominion to Israel here and now?" The answer St Luke has preserved is very instructive: "It is not for you to know the times and seasons which the Father has fixed by his own authority. Enough for you, that the Holy Spirit will come upon you, and you will receive strength from him; you are to be my witnesses in Jerusalem and throughout Judaea, in Samaria, yes, and to the ends of the earth" (Acts 1. 7-8).

Jerusalem, the central point towards which the whole history of the Jewish people converged, the city to which Jesus had come to consummate his sacrifice—a prophet, he had said, should not die outside Jerusalem—is considered by him after his resurrection as no more than the starting point for the universal expansion of the Church which was to come into existence there on the day of Pentecost. When the preaching of the Gospel had reached all the shores of the Mediterranean basin, the capture of Jerusalem by Titus and the destruction of the Temple would indicate that the Old Covenant had come to an end.

But Christ was not to preside in person over the coming to fruition of the seed he had sown. "God, then," declared Peter in his speech to the people on the morning of the day of Pentecost, "has raised up this man, Jesus, from the dead; we are all witnesses of it. And now, exalted at God's right hand, he has claimed from his Father his promise to bestow the Holy Spirit; and he has poured out that Spirit, as you can see and hear for yourselves" (Acts 2. 32-3). The visible mission of the Man-God, strictly limited as regards time and space, was followed by the invisible mission of the Spirit, henceforward co-extensive with the life of the human race and moving outward from Jerusalem after it had overcome a series of obstacles.

The first of these obstacles, strange though it may seem, was the friendship that had grown up between Christ and his apostles and the nostalgic longing for the familiar life they had known with the Master. This longing was expressed on Ascension Day in their lingering gaze towards the heavens into which Jesus had just disappeared. Yet he had warned them during the Last Supper: "And yet I can truly say that it is better for you I should go away; he who is to befriend you will not come to you unless I do go, but if only I make my way there, I will send him to you" (John 16. 7).

These mysterious words seem to set the mission of the Son and that of the Spirit in opposition to one another and appear to suggest that it was necessary for the first to end before the second began. They point out a contrast which must have had a profound effect on the apostles, a contrast between a visible and an invisible presence, between the certitude acquired by sight and the certitude born of faith. Yet the lesson given by the risen Lord to the unbelieving Thomas: "Blessed are those who have not seen, and yet have learned to believe", teaches us that the act of faith, inspired in the believer by the Holy Spirit, has a higher spiritual value than the psychological certitude engendered by a material presence. It can also be more efficacious and Peter was to have experience of this. We have only to listen to his words to the lame beggar near the Beautiful Gate of the Temple: "Silver and gold are not mine to give, I give thee what I can. In the name of Jesus Christ of Nazareth, rise up and walk" (Acts 3. 6). He was clearly certain that the miracle would take place. He was fully aware of the authority conferred on him by the invisible presence of the Spirit which had come down upon him on the morning of Pentecost. What a contrast is here between this and his hesitation to go forward to meet Jesus on the turbulent waters of the lake!

Once this first obstacle had been surmounted, others arose and took much longer to overcome. From his adolescent years, the Jewish child was trained to have a hearty detestation of pagans in whom he saw, not only the enemies of his race, but also the adversaries of God himself. In order to keep the Jewish people separated from them, the Mosaic law had set up numerous barriers among which restrictions concerning food played an important part. Faithful observance in this matter was a duty in conscience even under foreign domination. The aged Eleazar had chosen to be beaten to death rather than to pretend to eat pork.

Hence it is easy to understand Peter's spontaneous reaction when, in a symbolic vision, he received an order from heaven to disobey the ritual prohibition: "Rise up, Peter, lay about thee and eat. It cannot be, Lord, answered Peter; never in my life have I eaten anything profane, anything unclean. . . . It is not for thee to call anything profane, which God has made clean." And at that very instant, so that the meaning of this vision might be made clear, messengers from Cornelius, a Roman centurion, came to fetch Peter. Obedient to the inner word which ordered him to follow them to Caesarea, Peter understood the meaning of the vision and consented to sit down at the pagan's table: "You know well enough, he told them, that a Jew is contaminated if he consorts with one of another race, or visits him; but God has been shewing me that we ought not to speak of any man as profane or unclean; and so, when I was sent for, I came without demur" (Acts 10. 13–15, 28–9).

Unfortunately, difficulties on this score were to recur later. Even Peter himself was to behave in a manner inconsistent with his earlier decision and Paul was to reproach him on this account. It was to be more particularly Paul's mission to open wide the doors of the Church to the pagans.

Paul had received from the Holy Spirit himself the order to carry the Gospel to the pagans. This had happened one day at Antioch during the celebration of the liturgy by the local Church. St Luke tells us:

> The Church at Antioch had as its prophets and teachers Barnabas, and Simon who was called Niger, and Lucius of Cyrene, and Manahen, foster-brother of Herod the tetrarch, and Saul. These were offering worship to God and fasting, when the Holy Spirit said, I must have Barnabas and Saul dedicated to the work to which I have called them. Thereupon

they fasted and prayed and laid their hands on them, and so took leave of them. And they, sent on their travels by the Holy Spirit, went down to Seleucia, and from there took ship for Cyprus. (Acts 13. 1–4.)

[Thus began Paul's first mission. He was therefore justified in saying at a later date:] He whose power had enabled Peter to become the apostle of the circumcised, had enabled me to become the apostle of the Gentiles. And so, recognizing the grace God had given men, they joined their right hands in fellowship with Barnabas and myself; the Gentiles were to be our province, the circumcised theirs (Gal. 2. 8–9).

Further, St Paul was fully conscious of having been personally chosen by God to reveal to the infant Church the universal character of the salvation brought by Christ. As he meditated at leisure, during the period of his captivity in Rome, on the apostolic work he had done in the course of his three missions, he wrote to these whom he had brought to the light of faith "Briefly, yet so as to let you see how well I have mastered this secret of Christ's. It was never made known to any human being in past ages, as it has now been revealed by the Spirit to his holy apostles and prophets" (Eph. 3. 4–5).

This mystery which Paul had been destined to make known is that of the restoration of the unity of the human family through the Incarnation of the Son of God. This unity which formed part of the original plan of creation, had been broken by sin. While the pagans had refused to recognize their divine origin, and had given themselves over to their own perverse devices and the unholy desires of their hearts, the Jews, to whom God had granted the grace to know his oneness and to benefit by a law which revealed his will to them, had continually transgressed against the latter. There was a universal need for redemption and the reconciliation of Jews and pagans was the obvious consequence of their common ransom through the death of Christ on the Cross.

The universal scope of the redemption grew wider still in

the thought of St Paul and attained cosmic proportions. Christ is not only the Head of a spiritual community in which ethnic and social differences no longer have any meaning, but his primacy also extends over the whole of the cosmos which was created through and for him and whose unity he ensures: "It was God's good pleasure to let all completeness dwell in him, and through him to win back all things, whether on earth or in heaven, into union with himself, making peace with them through his blood, shed on the cross" (Col. 1. 19–20).

Man's sin has involved the universe in a state of servitude and the universe painfully labours to free itself from this in order to share in the liberty of the children of God. It is for the believer to understand and bear his part in this suffering of the world, and to cooperate in its liberation.

St Paul's doctrine, and the sympathy with which he approached the "nations" to which the Holy Spirit sent him, reveal several lessons which will be of great value in our efforts to solve the problem with which this book is concerned.

Everything in the universe is of a piece, is recapitulated by Christ in his person whose two natures, the human and the divine, are united without merging into one another. Nothing specifically human has been rejected by him, nothing should be treated by us with disdain; the true olive needs to be grafted on to the stock of the wild olive.

The universal scope of the redemption embraces time as well as space. By contrast with Christ's mission, which was confined to a period of some ten years, the mission of the Spirit, beginning on the morning of Pentecost, will last until the glorious return of him who left us on Ascension Day. Redemption, which comes to the successive generations as they enter this world, is not linked to the passing forms characteristic of different civilizations. The latter may evolve and at each period all the deeply human values in them are capable of being incorporated by God into the plan of his providence.

The law of work, in the form in which it was promulgated by God, after Adam had sinned, continues in force: "In the sweat of thy face shalt thou eat bread." But the quest for our daily bread has led to an innumerable variety of techniques that have succeeded one another down the course of the ages.

The progress of such techniques is now linked to the reflective operation of the mind which is increasingly penetrating the inner properties of matter and is able to make these serve increasingly higher forms of activity.

The name "Science" is commonly used today to indicate this reflective operation. For the Christian, science's claims to nobility are those of the law of human work, a law willed by the Father, sanctified by the Son during his stay among us, and the destinies of which will always be directed by the Spirit.

PART II

THE ENCOUNTER BETWEEN
CHRISTIANITY AND SCIENCE IN
THE COURSE OF HISTORY

CHAPTER IV

THE ARISTOCRATIC CHARACTER OF GREEK SCIENCE AND ITS CONTEMPT FOR TECHNOLOGY

As Bergson so clearly pointed out, the first flight of human intelligence was directed towards utilitarian ends: *homo faber* came before *homo sapiens*. As the well-known proverb says: *Primum vivere, deinde philosophari.*

Among primitive techniques, those which dealt with the measurement of space and time or which made use of it, were certainly prior to the speculative discoveries that gave rise to arithmetic and geometry. Are we then to conclude that the scientific mind,, characterized as it is by the search for intelligibility and by the demand for demonstration, is the result of reflection on these techniques, a reflection without any interest in utilitarianism?

That its origins lie here is confirmed by a commentary on Euclid's *Elements* written in the fifth century of our era by the neo-Platonist philosopher Proclus, but using an older document from the hand of an author living in the first century B.C., whose name was Geminus. Here is a summary of its teaching.

According to a generally accepted tradition, the Egyptians were the original inventors of geometry which owes its existence to the measurement of plots of ground that had continually to be restored because of the flood waters of the Nile which carried away the boundary stones between different properties. Thales apparently brought geometry from Egypt to Hellas and himself made several discoveries. He also prepared the way for the discovery of several other facts by his successors. Finally Pythagoras transformed this branch of study and made it a liberal education by moving on to the plane of higher principles and searching for abstract proofs. The discovery of surds and the construction of regular polyhedra is attributed to him.

Today this tradition has to be accepted with considerable reservations. We now have at our disposal several very ancient documents which give us an exact idea of the knowledge acquired by the Egyptian calculators. The best known and the most complete of these documents is the papyrus known as Rhind's, which was deciphered in about 1870 by Professor Eisenlohr of Heidelberg. This text was written about 1660 B.C. by a scribe named Ahmes and is itself only a copy of a much older document. We are therefore led to think that in the interval between the two versions no essential progress had been made in the art of calculation.

Ahmes' methods of calculation are very primitive. Although he made use of the decimal system for writing down numbers, the Egyptian calculator did not conceive the idea of making a table of the products of the first ten numbers once and for all and then of using them for further multiplications. He confines himself to simple duplication, repeated a certain number of times and completed by additions. Thus, in order to multiply a given number by five, Ahmes doubles it twice in succession, thus multiplying it by four, and then adds the number to the product of this multiplication. It is difficult to see how the mind could rise from so elementary a procedure to the abstract reasoning of arithmetic.

Other very ancient civilizations, for instance those of India and of China, carried the development of the art of calculation much further but never, in the course of their long history, achieved a work comparable to that of Euclid.

We must not therefore seek the origins of the scientific spirit in Greece (penetrated as it was by rationality and free of all concern for industrial application) in the field of the techniques of measurement and calculation. It must be attributed rather to the search for a unitary concept of the cosmos.

Before Socrates invited his compatriots to turn to the study of man, the first thinkers of Hellas were *Physiologists* who attributed to a primordial element—water (Thales), air (Anaximenes), fire (Heraclitus)—the origin of all the transformations which had led to the emergence from chaos of a concordant universe. The partly legendary personality of Pythagoras belongs to this line of thinkers. For lack of authentic documents concerning him, we turn to Aristotle for some interesting facts about those who called themselves Pythagoreans.

Those known as Pythagoreans began to busy themselves with mathematical researches and, once they had made considerable progress in this field, were led by their studies to take as principles of all existing things those which are used by the mathematical sciences. As the first principles in these sciences are necessarily numbers, they thought they could find in the latter many more analogies with what exists or is in a process of becoming in the world, than can be found in fire, air or water. . . .

After they had discovered that the properties and relations of musical harmonies correspond with numerical relations and that, in other natural phenomena, similar correspondences can be found with numbers, they arrived at the conviction that *numbers are elements of everything that exists and that the whole of the heavens is nothing but proportion and harmony* (Mdt A, 5, 985 b, 24 sq.).

Doubtless there was an exaggerated realism in this conviction, which, in any case, was to come to grief when irrational quantities were discovered, namely, quantities that are geometrically defined but whose relationship cannot be expressed by means of a numerical fraction. Nevertheless the project of reducing sense experience to mathematics, so as to introduce into it elements of rationality and to express the interdependence of phenomena through their relationships, was in the course of time to prove immensely fruitful.

Unfortunately, far from seeking to perfect, with this aim in mind, the concrete methods of measurement and calculation, as our modern physicists do, the Greeks, following Plato's lead, had nothing but contempt for what they disdainfully called logistics and mensuration. To these arts they opposed what they held were the only genuine sciences, arithmetic, the science of the abstract properties of numbers, and geometry, the science of intelligible figures, which Plato placed in a transcendent world, as an object of pure contemplation.

In this connection, however, things began to change at the period known as the Hellenistic, with Archimedes in whose birthplace, Syracuse, Athens' disdain for technology was not shared. We know the inventions that tradition attributes to him and by whose means he helped his fellow citizens to defend their city during a long siege which preceded the final, victorious assault of the Romans, and was followed by the violent death of the national hero.

These achievements, however, are not sufficient to earn the title of engineer for Archimedes. He remains essentially a geometer but one who had the audacity to introduce mechanics —in Plato's view an art and not a science—into geometry. It was thus that he defined the spiral which bears his name as the movement at a constant speed of a point on an upright which itself rotates with a uniform movement.

But it was not without experiencing scruples at striking a blow against the Platonic principles that Archimedes allowed himself to infringe them. "By means of mechanics", he wrote to Eratosthenes, a scientist of Alexandria, "I have often discovered propositions which I have then proved geometrically, since the method in question did not provide a genuine demonstration."

The audacity of the Syracusan geometer therefore had its limits. They were doubtless due to the influence of an environment in which the Platonic doctrine was supreme. Although he deserves credit for unashamedly practising an inductive mathematics, Archimedes maintained the preeminence of intelligibility and remained faithful to the rational spirit that characterized the scientific mentality prevalent at the time of his birth.

What, in the Hellas of the fifth century before Christ, was the origin of this disdain for technology and the proud isolation in which Greek thought wrapped itself as far as they were concerned? In the course of a discussion on this point with the *Société française de Philosophie*, E. Meyerson insisted— and in my opinion, rightly so—on the existence in Greece of the institution of slavery and on the fact that at Athens in particular all activity in connection with industrial production devolved on slaves. Typical observations, placed by Plato in the mouths of the persons in his dialogues, bear witness to the degrading character attributed to technical operations by the élite of the free classes of the population. And Aristotle thought slavery could be justified by arguing that servile work would be indispensable "as long as the weaver's shuttle does not move of its own accord".

Our historical perspective allows us today to reverse Aristotle's remark and to say that, as long as slavery lasted, the mind of the learned did not address itself to discovering a mechanism capable of making the shuttle move of its own accord. The automata and other ingenious pieces of apparatus manufactured in the first century of our era by Heron of Alexandria were superficial imitations to satisfy ear and eye, but no effort was made to replace human by efficient mechanical movements, nor, therefore, was this successfully achieved. Only engines of war were in any way efficient and that only for purposes of destruction. Even so, their efficiency was limited and Archimedes' inventions were not sufficient to save his country from defeat.

Yet in the disinterested character of the scientific spirit as it came into existence and developed in Greece, there is an undeniable nobility and even an affinity with the disinterestedness preached by Christ to his disciples.

There is one form of detachment which is as necessary for the scientist as for the Christian, and that is *detachment from personal utilitarian ends.* By linking these two adjectives—and it is essential to do so—I intend to convey that both the Christian spirit and the scientific spirit are incompatible with the lure of wealth. This is the meaning of the eulogy addressed long ago to Pythagoras by Aristoxenes, "you have lifted numbers above the realm of merchandise". This too is the lesson contained in the gesture of Christ driving the merchants from the Temple.

In both cases we are witnessing the advancement of a value which must be pure of all alloy, namely, *the search for truth.* Whether this truth is only partial and abstract like that of a theorem in geometry, or the concrete and total truth of our attitude to God and to the world, *truth must be sought after for its own sake,* with no thought of the personal advantages we might gain from possessing it.

This state of mind, when it exists, already establishes an affinity between the scientist and the Christian. This is why we pay homage, in a spirit of respect and brotherhood, to the example of disinterestedness set us throughout their lives by Pierre and Marie Curie. Whatever may have been the reasons

for their unbelief—and we have no authority to pass judgement in this respect—we are grateful to them for having set
the pursuit of truth, however partial it may appear to us,
above that of money and, what is more rare, that of honours.

This detachment from money and honours, which is necessary for both the scientist and the Christian, does not in any
way allow us to conclude *that truth is essentially sterile*. As
regards *scientific truth*, it is precisely in this respect that the
Greek genius restricted its own progress. In geometry, as in
the plastic arts, Plato's fellow countrymen were too sensitive
to the beauty of form. They persisted in isolating immediate
images of the universe and idealizing them. They then found
it easier to analyse them under the form of simplified relationships and so experience the joy of understanding. It is this
insistence on idealization which is likely to lead to sterility.

In nature geometrical forms are seldom to be found in all
their simplicity. Everything in nature is physical and so
irregular; above all, nothing in nature is motionless. We must
aim to acquire mastery over the universe if we are to understand it in all its complexity and to discover the laws of its
evolution. Archimedes had an inkling that such a requirement
existed even though he remained too attached to Platonism.
In any case, he had no imitators. It was only in the person of
Leonardo da Vinci that he was to find a successor many
centuries later.

The spirit of the Gospel is of a higher order. It contains
truth in its totality and we are to be anxious only for the one
thing necessary. Yet Christ said: "Seek first the kingdom of
God" and then immediately added: "and the rest will be added
to you", not as something superfluous, for our heavenly Father
is well aware that this "rest" is indispensable for us, since
food and clothing are meant. But it is precisely because our
heavenly Father knows this and his providence governs the
world, that while we occupy our time—as Christ worked to
provide food for his mother and as Mary worked, weaving

with her own hands the seamless garment for which the executioners of her Son cast lots—we are never to be pre-occupied and anxious. The only thing forbidden to the Christian is anxiety and desire to possess more and more, or the exaggerated fear that he will not have enough. Free of these, his thoughts and desires can rise to higher things.

This teaching is on a very high plane and yet it is very sensible. It frees the mind while leaving the hands tied to their task. And the Christian takes good care not to follow Plato and Aristotle in despising manual work.

This doctrine was most faithfully implemented in the institution of monasticism. After the upheavals that followed the barbarian invasions it was in the monasteries that the fruitful alliance between manual and intellectual work was achieved in that atmosphere of supreme spiritual liberty which is, and will continue to be until the end of time, the most evident sign of the action of the Holy Spirit.

Yet efforts have been made to show that Christianity is responsible for the decay of Greek science. Thus in his recent book, *Histoire de la Science*, Maurice Daumas writes:

> After this final brilliant achievement (the astronomical studies of Ptolemy and Diophantes' arithmetic), the School of Alexandria entered on a period of definite decline. The history of the town again became characterized by pillage, conflagra-tions and massacres. But the chief cause of decline was the progress of Christianity. Teaching in the university was still, it is true, under the aegis of polytheism, but though neither for-bidden nor persecuted, it gradually lost its status.

In his *La Géometrie grecque*, Paul Tannery wrote of this period and made rather more careful distinctions:

> It was the age immediately before that of Constantine and the triumph of Christianity. It has been said with some justifica-tion that the major revolution which followed was fatal to Science. It is certain that from that time forward mankind

was offered a very different ideal from that which Plato and
Aristotle had set forth so brilliantly, namely the life of the
man of learning as the contemplation of *theory for its own
sake*. But...the accusation against Christianity is without
foundation. Just as the barbarians experienced no difficulty in
bringing about the ruin of Greco-Roman society, which had
already collapsed from within, Christianity had only to
liquidate the affairs of the bankrupt official philosophy after
the century of the Antonines. The Platonic ideal had long since
given way to that of the Stoics, which was fundamentally
utilitarian and so opposed to science, in spite of the outward
appearances of its lofty moral system.

A Dutch historian, E. J. Dijksterhuis, in an inquiry extending to the age of the Fathers[1] attempts a more profound
analysis of the relations which were established during this
period between Christianity and the natural sciences. While
he refrains from attributing to the Fathers of the Church a
system of thought radically hostile to the study of nature and
while admitting even the presence in their writings of the statement that this study is a duty for the Christian, the author
considers that their most common attitude is one of reserve
and waiting. He identifies three reasons for this which I now
propose to examine here.

In the first place, Christianity is a *doctrine of salvation*.
Before all else the Christian must be concerned for the salvation of his soul and, as St Basil observed, has no need to
trouble to find out whether the earth is a sphere, a cylinder or
a disc.

On the other hand, science must submit to *the authority of
Holy Scripture*, in particular to its teaching on God's creation
of the universe. The Christian must pay homage to the
Creator and not to a personification of nature.

Finally, the *Platonism of the Fathers* diverted their interests
from reality as it appears to the senses. They were under the

[1] E. J. Dijksterhuis, *Die Mechanisierung des Weltbildes* (Berlin, 1956).

spell of the doctrine of ideas although they considered these as existing not in a world of their own but in the divine thought. The identification of the demiurge with the Creator completed this synthesis of Plato and the Bible.

Although I do not deny that there is some truth in these remarks, yet they seem to me to convey a narrow view of Christianity and so require a few comments. I shall link these with the three objections just summarized.

Christianity is a doctrine of salvation, but it is much more— it is a *history of salvation*. Christ came at a given moment in time to set up the kingdom of God in this world. This kingdom is a social fact, the Church, which all men are invited to enter. She is assured of the assistance of the Holy Spirit and of her own continued existence until the end of time. The universal character of Pentecost goes beyond individual salvation which is much more akin to Plotinian asceticism than to the spirit of the Gospel.

Although in the sixteenth century a rigid interpretation of Holy Scripture was invoked to justify Galileo's condemnation, it would be an anachronism to read this back into the patristic period. The exegetical work of Origen testifies to the freedom with which the sacred books were interpreted at that time. Sacred Scripture moreover was not only the *lex credendi*; for the faithful it was above all a *lex orandi*. It was at this time that St Ambrose inaugurated at Milan the custom of the antiphonal chanting of the psalms by the people.

The psalms are a summary of the whole of the Old Testament in whose context they came into existence and, through them, this context had a profound influence on the sensibility of the whole of Christendom. The theologians themselves, although occupied with speculative tasks, did not escape its effect. Claude Tresmontant reaches the following conclusions at the end of his *Essai sur la pensée hébraïque* (Paris, 1953), p. 168:

Catholic theology, in spite of all opposition, in relation to and in conflict with all the intellectual temptations arising from the prevalent philosophical climate, preserved the great themes of biblical metaphysics, namely, the eminent goodness of sensible reality, the necessary instrumentality of this sensible reality in the economy of our salvation ... the instrumental rôle of concrete historical reality.

Thus the third objection is already answered. According to it, the Fathers' Platonism diverted their interests from reality as it appears to the senses. In one particular alone the Church owes a debt to Platonic philosophy. From it she learned to direct the attention of Hebrew thought to the fate of man immediately after death. This she was able to do because of the Greek idea of the spirituality and immortality of the soul. But we must immediately add that, in contradiction to Greek philosophy and in spite of the sarcastic remarks of Paul's hearers on the Areopagus, she made the future resurrection of the body an article of her Creed, on the strength of the historical fact of the resurrection of Christ which is both the guarantee of the Christian's faith and the foundation of his hope.

So that if, in the patristic period, mathematics and the natural sciences were in the process of decay, it was above all because there were no original minds capable of directing into new channels disciplines whose original impetus was spent.

Moreover, among the authors of compilations at the end of this period, we find such Christians as John Philopon at Alexandria and, at Rome, Boëthius, the friend of Pope John I and translator of Nicomachus of Gerasa whose books were held in great repute in the Middle Ages to which they handed on a part of the achievement of ancient science.

CHAPTER V

MECHANICS THE RESULT
OF CHRISTIAN
ENCOURAGEMENT OF
TECHNOLOGY

In 1634 there was published in Paris, by the bookseller Guenon, a work by Galileo entitled, *The Mechanics of Galileo, Civil Engineer and Mathematician to the Duke of Florence*. It had been written in Italian but had not yet appeared in Italy where it was published only after Galileo's death. Hence the book saw the light for the first time in Paris, translated and edited by the indefatigable Fr Mersenne.

He was a strange figure, this Minim friar who had come to Paris towards the end of the year 1619 with the intention of making mincemeat of the atheists. His warlike ardour was tempered by a love of music with which he connected the sciences that seemed to him to be related to it, in particular mathematics and physics. He had an inquiring if untidy mind; he was a conversationalist of charm and was fond of welcoming visitors, and his cell in the friary on the Place Royale (now Place des Vosges) soon became the rallying-point of all those who, whether living in Paris or merely passing through the city, were interested in the movement of ideas and in the progress of the experimental sciences.

But to return to Galileo who, given the literary customs of the time, was doubtless not consulted regarding the publication of his book in France; the latter's title shows the part played by technology in the revival of the scientific spirit in the seventeenth century. At its beginnings, mechanics was still only "the science of mechanical devices" as is shown by the title of the first chapter "in which we find the preface that demonstrates the utility of machines". Chapter VI is devoted to the steelyard, to the balance and the lever, chapter VII to the lathe, the wheel, the windlass and other instruments of the same sort. Chapter VIII deals with force and the use of pulleys, chapter IX with the screw and chapter X with Archimedes' screw for raising water.

But the anxiety to provide a rational explanation, which was characteristic of the scientific spirit when it arose in Greece, is also found in this study, although it is almost entirely devoted to technology. It appears in chapter IV "in which one of the general principles of mechanical devices is explained". The matter at issue is the rule governing the equilibrium of a lever whose arms are unequal. The functioning of all machines, in Galileo's estimation, can be reduced to the principle according to which "unequal weights in fact have an equal weight and produce an equilibrium when they are suspended at unequal distances which are in inverse ratio to the weights in question".

The urge to make things intelligible is more generally present than the anxiety to provide a rational mathematical explanation. How is it possible to grasp *a priori* the fact that a very heavy load can be lifted by a very small force? There is nothing simpler, answers Galileo, provided we presuppose that it is possible to "divide the load into so many parts that the force in question can move one of these, for then it will move them all one after the other. It therefore follows that the

smallest force in the world can move any weight we like."
But, as it is not always possible to divide the load, it is at this
point that the use and the purpose of machines become
apparent. "Machines are useful in handling heavy loads at
one go without dividing them up, as we do on the frequent
occasions when we have plenty of time but little available
force. This is why length of time makes up for lack of force."

By introducing the question of time, Galileo complicated
research into the laws of equilibrium which is concerned with
a problem in "statics", by bringing up a much more difficult
problem, that of dynamics, which includes the notion of
velocity. We shall see that Descartes eliminated time and so
made statics entirely geometrical.

On October 5th, 1637, in an answer to a request from his
Dutch friend Constantine Huygens, the father of the great
geometrician, Christian Huygens, Descartes added to his letter
a short document entitled, *Explication des engins par l'aide
desquels on peut, avec une petite force, lever un fardeau fort
pesant* ("a description of machines with which, using only a
small force, it is possible to lift a very heavy load").
Descartes's desire for rational explanations was as great as
or greater than Galileo's. He published his *Discours de la
Méthode* during this period and he proposed to reduce the
explanation of all machines to one single principle: "The
invention of all machines is founded on one single principle
alone: the same force which can raise a weight of say
100 pounds to a height of two feet, can also raise a weight of
200 pounds to the height of one foot, or one of 400 pounds
to the height of six inches, and so on, provided the force is
applied."

The term "force" as used in this text is ambiguous and
corresponds to what we now call *the work done by a force*.
In fact, Descartes explained this during the following year in
a letter to Mersenne: "It must above all be borne in mind that

I have been speaking of the force which is used to lift a weight to a certain height. This force has always two dimensions. I was not speaking of the force which is used at each stage to support the weight. This force has only one dimension."

Descartes adds:

> As for those who say that I should have taken velocity into consideration, as does Galileo, rather than space, in my explanation of machines, I think—between ourselves—that they are people who talk as the fit takes them, without any understanding of this subject. Though it is obvious that more force is needed to lift a body very quickly than to lift it very slowly, yet it is pure imagination to say that the force must be exactly double if the velocity is to be doubled.

Yet Galileo's supporters insisted on their point of view and pointed out that, in simple machines, the movements of the two points, that to which the power is applied and that at which the resistance takes place, are simultaneous. Hence there is a ratio between the length of the paths covered and the velocities developed. Descartes did not contest the fact, but replied that to introduce time in this way into a problem towards whose rational solution it contributed nothing beyond what was already involved in the consideration of the areas covered, made the problem of equilibrium inseparable from a much greater and more complex problem: "For it is impossible to say anything of value concerning velocity without having given a genuine explanation of what weight is and so, at the same time, of the whole system of the universe".

In the pages that follow, we shall see how correct this observation was. At the moment we merely note with what ease Descartes and Galileo pass from the most concrete considerations to rational investigations. The former patently suggested the latter and we at length find that the gulf between technics and science has been bridged. And this had never been done by the Greeks. It is their alliance which gave birth to the new science of mechanics, centred round the two key-notions of force and movement. Velocity was soon to join them, when reflection and geometrization turned to the problem of falling bodies and the movement of projectiles.

It was a professor, Gilles Personne de Roberval, "Regius Professor of Mathematics at the Collège de Maître Gervais and holder of the chair of Ramus in the Collège Royal de France", who was to complete the geometrization of mechanics by isolating it from the concrete investigation of machines and by giving to his book the form of a treatise on mechanics. Even if, in this kind of work, as Duhem remarks, a profusion of axioms, a learned and complicated deductive apparatus, sometimes only serve to cloak certain essential hypotheses, yet the attempt witnesses to a legitimate search for clarity and exactitude.

This treatise on mechanics was published in 1636, thanks again to Fr Mersenne who incorporated it in one of his own books. It has only thirty-six pages, but Roberval was working on a much more complete treatise, in which he was aiming to construct "a mechanics, which would be entirely new from top to bottom". The edifice would be completed in eight stages; that is, it would be in eight volumes.

This great treatise was never published, since the author was waiting for the right moment to make his works public. This would be at such time as any candidates presented themselves for the chair which he held, since appointment to the latter was by triennial competition. By a strange irony of fate, the man who dreamed of becoming the lawgiver of mechanics is known to the majority of our contemporaries only as the maker of the type of scales he invented five years before his death and which is found in all the grocers' shops.

But since Roberval's time, the ideal of a rational mechanics has not ceased to haunt the minds of mathematicians who have taken over this science and organized it on the model of a geometrical treatise by means of a learned series of theorems

which d'Alembert in the eighteenth century still could not
decide whether to consider as necessary or as contingent
truths.

The very notion of a rational mechanics was, I repeat,
entirely foreign to Greek thought. In Plato's system of education, the description of machines did not rank higher than
elementary instruction in which it was on a level with
mensuration, the practical science of the measurement of
length and surfaces, and logistics, the art of calculation. At
a higher level of instruction, geometry, took the place of
mensuration and arithmetic was substituted for logistics. But
no place was reserved for a rational discipline with machines
as its subject. The élite among Greek thinkers was not to
bother itself about them.

More than ten centuries passed before the aristocratic
contempt of the Greek philosophers for manual work was
replaced by a receptive attitude which included it in an
integral conception of philosophy and wisdom. This was
possible because, from that time onward, wisdom was Christian and human work was a recognized value in the process
that leads to divine wisdom, since Christ and St Paul had
worked with their hands.

We were able to draw attention to this development on the
strength of evidence provided by Hugh of St Victor, and to
point out certain of its details with the help of Fr Roger
Baron's thesis recently published.[1]

In two books that appeared one after the other in the course
of the twelfth century, the *Epitome in Philosophiam*, written
in the form of a dialogue, and the *Didascalicon*, which is a
genuine treatise, Hugh divides the sciences into four sections.
First come ethics and theorics; the third place is assigned to

[1] Roger Baron, *Science et sagesse chez Hugues de Saint-Victor*
(Paris, 1957). Cf. in particular, ch. II: "Les arts, les sciences et la
philosophie", pp. 35 seq.

mechanics and the series ends with logic. Mechanics is defined by Hugh as "the wisdom which directs human actions". It in its turn is subdivided into seven different sciences on the obvious precedent of the classic septenary of the seven liberal arts. The sciences are: wool manufacture, the manufacture of arms, navigation, agriculture, hunting, medicine and the science of games (*theatrica*).

Each of the mechanical sciences is reviewed rapidly but conscientiously in a survey which "will doubtless be of some value for historians of social life in the Middle Ages and of the handing down of ancient traditions" (*op. cit.*, p. 61). Hugh of St Victor also wrote a *Practica Geometriae* (published in 1956 in the review *Osiris* by M. Roger Baron). It deals with experimental methods of measuring: altimetry, planimetry, cosmometry or the measurement of the circumference of the celestial and terrestrial spheres.

Hugh of St Victor, as is obvious, set himself to survey the whole of human knowledge with an interest that reveals his breadth of mind. All specifically human acts, in his view, have wisdom as their informative principle and so are matter for philosophy which he defines as the search for a type of wisdom for which nothing human remains foreign.

And it is from the period between the ninth to the twelfth centuries that we date the discovery of such kinds of motive power as that supplied by animals, water and air. The harnessing of horses was rationalized by the invention of the halter. Watermills and windmills became common and their uses increasingly extended. As Guy Beaujouan writes: "contrary to a very widespread opinion, the burning faith of the Middle Ages did not have as its corollary an indifferent attitude towards practical realities" ("La science dans l'Occident mediéval chrétien", in *Histoire Générale des sciences*, Part III, ch. VIII, p. 360). The interest in technology shown at this time prepared the way for the emergence of a new science, Mechanics.

The discovery that it was possible to inaugurate a rational science of machines and, in a more general way, a science of the different circumstances in which movement is generated, is the great intellectual achievement of the seventeenth century. It not only established between the work of the mind and manual tasks, between reason and experience, a link which will never be broken and which ensures a process of cross-fertilization, but it also opened the way to a vast area of knowledge reaching out, in the phrase of Descartes quoted above, to the whole "system of the universe".

This is the one point to which Christian Huygens, a "lapsed" disciple of Descartes, remained faithful after he had partly abandoned the rest of his master's teaching. At the beginning of his *Treatise on Light*, Huygens defined the "true philosophy" as that "in which the cause of all natural effects is conceived in terms of mechanics". And he added: "In my opinion, unless this is done, we have to give up all hope of ever understanding physics" (quoted by P. Duhem in *Evolution de la Mécanique* (Paris, 1903), p. 1).

But what is meant by "in terms of mechanics"? It is at this point that ideas differed from the outset and then continued to evolve with the passage of time. A classification of these ideas is therefore relevant and I shall now provide one with the help of E. J. Dijksterhuis's book, already mentioned, and of Robert Lenoble's thesis on Fr Mersenne (*Mersenne ou la naissance du Mécanisme* (Paris, 1943)).

For Mersenne, to explain the world in terms of the play of mechanical forces is to guarantee the transcendent character of the knowledge of both salvation and religion. In fact, miracle is only recognizable as such if nature is subject to laws through which the divine government of the world is normally exercised: "The majority of the actions and movements which take place in nature are always of the same order and bear witness to the uniformity of the divine acts which cause them. Few people take this into consideration, as though it were no part of the duty of all men to instruct themselves in the laws which God causes nature to obey, and through which he governs the world that he has made for his own glory" (quoted by R. Lenoble, *op. cit.*, note on p. 447).

The world, as Mersenne sees it, is a vast machine and God the engineer who has designed it according to a plan of which the law of inertia is an essential characteristic. He has constructed the world in accordance with this plan and has set it in motion. Only experiment can bring us to a knowledge of the movements in the world as a whole. It was in the same spirit that Kepler and Newton desired to bear explicit witness to the Creator of the universe.

Descartes, Leibniz and, in the century of Voltaire himself, Maupertuis made reference to the wisdom of the Creator though in a more intellectualist, even rationalist manner, and from a teleological standpoint. Like a careful administrator, God has achieved his purposes by bringing into play certain principles of conservation and even a principle of "minimum action". In further chapters we shall see how these theological or teleological considerations were shown by experience to be external to the subject matter of classical physics and so were gradually eliminated.

Another movement is connected with the idea of the "mechanical model", a favourite notion of the English physicists who always looked for hidden mechanisms capable of accounting for the data of sense experience. To this tendency is due the important rôle attributed to the phenomena of impact and to vortex motion, whose use by Descartes is well known. But when we find physicists such as Huygens and Leibniz rejecting the Newtonian concept of attraction as *non-mechanical*, whereas the sum total of planetary movements deduced from it by Newton is the most lucid of the mechanical models for the visible phenomena of the celestial sphere, we wonder what remains of the whole notion of such a model apart from a mere appeal to the intuition of our imagination.

Huygens' thesis can only have one tenable meaning although he himself would have denied it. Yet history obliges us to accept it; "the terms of mechanics" that make possible an understanding of the sum total of physical movements in the universe are none other than the very concepts and fundamental laws of classical mechanics. Doubtless the latter has received a new orientation from the relativity theory, but it nonetheless presupposes our present view of the universe, a view now extending to the galaxies; and it guides our efforts to conquer planetary space.

CHAPTER VI

THE WITNESS OF NEWTON,

KEPLER AND EINSTEIN

Whereas for the atomism of Democritus all events occurring in the world consist of the movements of unalterable particles which develop according to no law and are linked with one another by chance alone, the universe conceived as a mechanism presupposes an intelligent designer who has adapted the parts to one another and then has set the whole in movement towards a predetermined end.

But mechanicalism, whose emergence was studied in the previous chapter, also contradicts another doctrine, very widespread in the sixteenth and seventeenth centuries, according to which the world was peopled with spirits or occult forces which man could control by magic. Fr Mersenne was fighting a battle on two fronts, on the one hand against atheistic materialism and on the other against a prevalent animism which recklessly debased the Aristotelian concept of nature.

This twofold struggle gave birth to a "theological mechanicalism" which teaches that the material world is only intelligible by means of the laws of movement, and sees these laws, when isolated and translated in mathematical form, as the expression of a creative mind. The doctrine may claim support from two famous scientists, Kepler and Newton, and we find a faint though authentic echo of it in Einstein's cosmic deism. This chapter is devoted to an examination and criticism of this view.

Johann Kepler was born on December 27th, 1571, in the little village of Magstadt, near Weil der Stadt in Württemberg. After successfully studying astronomy at Tübingen and in spite of financial worries, Kepler published in 1596 his first book whose aim was to reveal the *Mysterium cosmographicum*. In fact it revealed above all the Pythagorean and Platonist tendencies of its author's mind.

Kepler compared the then universally admitted existence of six planets moving round the sun (according to the Copernican theory, at increasing distances from Mercury to Saturn) to the mathematical existence of five regular polyhedra, and he imagined an interlocking process of such a character that each of these polyhedra was, in a determined order, inscribed in a sphere containing the trajectory of one of the planets, and circumscribed about the sphere bearing the trajectory of the next planet. In this way he thought he could account for the number of the planets and also for the numerical series of their distances from the sun.

In regard to the various speeds of circulation, Kepler later deduced their values from another intelligible source, namely, the relationships between the notes of the scale. Macrocosm and microcosm, the universe and human sensibility, were both dominated by the same harmony.

These comparisons seem arbitrary to the astronomers of the twentieth century, and indeed they are. But Kepler, unlike the scientist of today, did not have at his disposal a well-stocked catalogue of mathematical functions with various and well-known properties, from which, with a little inventiveness and a fair amount of good luck, could be picked out those that are most suited to the phenomena studied. He had no option but to attempt to compare the latter directly with the laws determined by known geometrical forms or by physical phenomena that had already been expressed mathematically.

On the other hand, Kepler showed himself very "modern" in his anxiety to verify hypotheses under consideration, and this by means of precise measurements. He himself analysed his own intellectual operations with the greatest clarity. He wrote:

> It is true that I play with symbols and that I have written a little book *Cabbala geometrica* which deals with ideas concerning nature, in the realm of mathematics. But while I play, I never forget that I am playing, for nothing is proved by symbols, no secret in the philosophy of nature is brought to light by mathematical signs. Only what is already known can be clarified in this way, only what has been established by convincing proofs that are not merely symbols. The latter are only useful to express the characteristics and the causes of the dependent relations between objects when compared with one another.

The convincing proofs Kepler desired were to be provided by the most remarkable observer of the time, the Danish astronomer, Tycho Brahé. Tycho Brahé had spent twenty years observing, night after night, the sky and the stars from an observatory constructed according to his own plans on the island of Hveen, which had been given him in fee by the king of Denmark, Frederick II. In this observatory, to which he had given the name *Uraniborg*, Tycho Brahé had installed a whole collection of instruments of astonishing size, which made it possible for him to make more accurate measurements of the position of the stars than had hitherto been secured.

But at the end of the sixteenth century, Tycho had fallen out of favour with Frederick II's successor and he was obliged to leave his Uraniborg observatory. He sought a new protector and found him at Prague in the person of Rudolph II. By a providential turn of events, Kepler had, at this same time, to leave Graz owing to an edict against the Protestants, and he too sought refuge in Prague, where Rudolph gave him to Tycho Brahé as his assistant. They worked together for a very short time, from February 1600 until October 1601, when Tycho died. However, Kepler was instructed by Rudolph to continue his master's work, and he inherited the immense documentation the latter had accumulated.

It was by utilizing Tycho's observations on the planet Mars that Kepler discovered that it was impossible to hold that Mars had a circular orbit. He evolved and then verified the hypothesis of an elliptical orbit. In 1609 he published his discovery in a new work entitled *Astronomia nova*, in which he began by enunciating the second of the laws which now bear his name, the law which asserts the uniformity of the "areolar velocity", that is, the velocity by which the surface swept out by the vector radius joining a planet to the sun varies. Kepler's third law which states that "the square of the time of revolution of any planet round the sun is proportional to the cube of its mean distance from the sun" was not enunciated until 1618, in a work whose title itself, *Harmonices Mundi*, shows how delighted Kepler was to return to the symbolist views of his younger days. It is not in this book, however, but in a passage at the end of the nineteenth chapter of the *Astronomia nova* that we find the most authentic expression of Kepler's genius:

> We have been granted by the divine goodness a scrupulous observer in Tycho Brahé whose measurements corrected by eight minutes the imperfect calculations of Ptolemy. We should accept with gratitude this gift of God and profit by it. We should do our best, on the strength of this proof of the inaccuracy of the ideas of antiquity, to give a true and definitive account of the movement of the heavens. It is along this path that I shall, in my own fashion, be the first to walk.... These eight minutes have in themselves opened the way to the renewal of the whole of astronomy; they have to a great extent become the foundation of the edifice.

These last lines are plainly prophetic if we remember that Kepler's laws form the historical point of departure of the

Newtonian synthesis and that today they have become quite simply the outcome of the mathematical expression given by Newton to the law of universal attraction.

But the passage also and above all reveals the profoundly religious temper of Kepler. His admiration and gratitude for his master Tycho Brahé are directed to God and his providence. The laws of planetary movement, whose importance for our systematic knowledge of the universe he already senses, were not, in his estimation, invented by him. He merely discovered them since, according to him, they pre-existed in the divine mind before they became apparent to his own. He therefore accepts them as a free gift from God.

His theological views go further still and his tendency to look for symbols gives them a more debatable anthropomorphic character. Before Newton, Kepler understood that to place the sun at one of the foci of the ellipses described around it by the planets is not a proposition in pure geometry but a fact in the existential order and requiring explanation. The function of this heavenly body is not merely to give light and warmth to the world of the planets, it also plays an active part in the maintenance of, and the periodical variations in, the velocities of the planets. This type of causality even offers the scientist the most perfect image of the primal causality exercised by the Creator.

Kepler pushes this comparison further and comes to the very threshold of the Trinitarian mystery. The sun is not only the immovable centre but the source of attraction of the planets, and so is the image of the Father. The whole body of fixed stars which forms the frame of reference within which we can follow the evolution of the planets, is the image of the Word. The force of attraction in the sun which flows over into space, and there directs the movement of the planets, is the image of the Holy Spirit.

Is this merely symbolism or a genuine comparison? Some have maintained that Kepler was a sun-worshipper. He himself forestalled such a misunderstanding: "My point of view is the following: I hold that the heavenly mechanism is not to be likened to a being whose nature is divine. Does anyone believe that a clock in working order deprives the artist who has made it of the glory of his work?"

The discovery of the divine thought and the manifestation of God's glory were undoubtedly the most powerful motives behind Kepler's scientific work. We may regret the survival in him of the Pythagoreanism which led him into endless reflections on the "harmonies of the universe". We may criticize as anthropomorphic his transference to God of the mathematical mode of expression characteristic of human thought; and finally, we may consider his attempted comparison between the Trinitarian mystery and the stellar universe as artificial and lacking in respect for the transcendence of the supernatural order. Yet we can only pay homage to the fervent piety which urged Kepler to compose the prayer he inserted in the first chapter of Book V of the *Harmonices mundi*:

Hitherto I have proclaimed the work of God the Creator. It now remains for me to close this series of demonstrations and at length to lift up to heaven my eyes and my hands, and as a devout suppliant to offer this prayer to the Father of Lights:

O thou who dost awaken within us by the light of nature, a desire for the light of grace, so that thou mayest lead us thereby to the light of glory, I give thee thanks, O Lord and Creator, who hast filled me with joy in that which thou hast made and given me gladness in the work of thy hands.

Now I have finished the work of my calling and have used all the powers of the talent thou hast given me. I have manifested the glory of thy works to the men who will read these demonstrations, at least in so far as the narrow limits of my understanding has been able to grasp their infinity. My mind has always sought to philosophize according to the truth.

If I have done anything unworthy of thy purposes, I who am but a worm, born and nourished in the filth of sin, inspire me to proclaim that which thou willest men to know, so that I may mend my ways.

If I have given place to temerity before the admirable beauty of thy works or if I have sought my own glory before men while I pursued a task destined to glorify thee, in thy gentle mercy, do thou pardon me.

And deign in thy goodness to grant that these demonstrations may redound to thy glory and work for the salvation of souls and not be a hindrance thereto.

Like Kepler, Newton in his scientific works also spoke of God, but in more emphatic tones which do not directly reveal the emotion of the scientist aware that he owes to God the inspiration which makes him an innovator and almost a prophet.

We are still more puzzled when we remember that the *Scholium generale*, which concludes the *Philosophiae naturalis principia mathematica*, and in which the author pays homage to the Creator, does not figure in the first edition published in 1687. It is only in the second edition, which appeared in 1713, that we find Newton anxious to attribute the order presiding over the organization of the universe, the sun, the planets and the comets, to the action of an all-powerful and intelligent Being substantially present everywhere and at all times—for there can be no action without presence—and whose wisdom and will account for the diversity which reigns throughout time and space.

Between 1687 and 1713 an event occurred which accounts for the belated insertion of this piece of apologetics. In 1691 Robert Boyle died. He was a celebrated physicist and chemist and also a convinced believer and had left in his will a sum of money to provide for an annual series of apologetic lectures. The first holder of this lectureship was Richard Bentley, who devoted his last three lectures to a description of Newton's cosmology with the intention of drawing from it arguments against atheism. Moreover, Bentley informed

Newton of his plan and put several questions to him in writing. To these the great scientist replied in four letters which were published much later in the 1757 edition of the *Opera Omnia*.[1]

Bentley's lectures showed the English public what use could be made of the phenomenon of universal attraction in establishing the fact of God's existence. In view of the success of these lectures, Newton decided to make use of the views put forward by Bentley, and did so first in his *Optics*[2] in 1706, then in 1713 when he inserted the *Scholium generale* in the second edition of the *Principia*.

The somewhat fortuitous character of Newton's apologetic may suggest that his belief in a personal God, however sincere it may have been, did not play an important part in the evolution of his system of thought, as had been the case with Kepler. A statement in his first letter to Bentley seems to bear this out:

> When I wrote my treatise about our system, I had an eye upon such principles as might work with considering men for the belief of a deity; and nothing can rejoice me more than to find it useful for that purpose. But if I have done the public any service this way, it is due to nothing but industry and patient thought.[3]

We shall be all the more inclined to take this view if we consider Newton as a forerunner of Auguste Comte's positivism, as does Léon Bloch in his thesis for the Sorbonne doctorate submitted in 1908 (*La Philosophie de Newton*, Paris, 1908). But this interpretation depends upon an anachronism

[1] The General Scholium and the four letters are printed in *Newton's Philosophy of Nature*, ed. H. S. Thayer (New York, Hafner, 1953), pp. 41 ff.

[2] This book first appeared in English and was only later translated into Latin (*Quaestiones Opticae*). The famous comparison between infinite space and God's *Sensorium* is found in question 28.

[3] *Newton's Philosophy of Nature*, p. 46.

against which E. A. Burtt in England, Mme Hélène Metzger in France and, more recently, René Dugas[4] have protested.

The principal argument used to prove that Newton was a positivist by anticipation is his famous phrase, *Hypotheses non fingo*. But what does it mean and on what occasion did he pronounce it? "Why", writes René Dugas, "did Newton declare war on hypotheses? Simply, so it would seem, because he had suffered much from them and not so that he might claim greater certitude for his own system." It is a fact that Newton suffered a great deal from the polemics in which he was engaged, particularly with Hooker, on the priority of the law of attraction in inverse ratio to the square of the distance, and on the theory of the composition of white light. It is thus easier to understand how he was led to insist on the experiments which were the basis of his theoretical ideas rather than on the precise characteristics of the latter which he always considered hypothetical. In fact, Newton put forward numerous hypotheses, such as that of ether in the spheres of optics, and on the nature of gravity, for he would never admit that the latter could operate at a distance without some intermediary agent.

Polemics also intensified the introverted nature of his character. His successor in the Cambridge chair, Whiston, used to say that Newton had the most diffident, reserved and touchy temperament he had ever come across.

But this impenetrable obscurity in Newton's thought had, as far as religion is concerned, a more fundamental origin. Very early in life, he ceased to believe in the Trinity, but, whereas Whiston, his successor at Cambridge and like himself a Unitarian, publicly proclaimed his convictions and so was deprived of his chair on the grounds of his Arianism, Newton,

[4] E. A. Burtt, *The Metaphysics of Sir Isaac Newton, An Essay on the Metaphysical Foundation of Modern Science* (London, 1925 and 1949). Hélène Metzger, *Attraction universelle et religion naturelle chez quelques commentateurs anglais de Newton* (Paris, 1938).

loaded with honours in London, jealously preserved his secret. It was confined to papers kept in a box. After his death, the editor of his *Complete Works* refused to use these, so horrified was he after only a glance at their contents.

In 1888, the mathematical section of these papers was bequeathed to the University of Cambridge. In 1936, the rest were sold by auction and Lord Keynes managed to secure some of those containing the anti-trinitarian writings. He was thus able, in a lecture given on the occasion of the third centenary of Newton's birth, to put forward the view of the great scientist's inner personality which he had derived from reading these papers:

> In the eighteenth century and since, Newton came to be thought of as the first and greatest of the modern age of scientists, a rationalist, one who taught us to think on the lines of cold and untinctured reason. I do not see him in this light. I do not think that anyone who has pored over the contents of that box which he packed up when he finally left Cambridge in 1696 and which, though partly dispersed, have come down to us, can see him like that. Newton was not the first of the age of reason. He was the last of the magicians, the last of the Babylonians and Sumerians, the last great mind which looked out on the visible and intellectual world with the same eyes as those who began to build our intellectual inheritance rather less than 10,000 years ago.... His deepest instincts were occult, esoteric, semantic—with profound shrinking from the world, a paralysing fear of exposing his thoughts, his beliefs, his discoveries in all nakedness to the inspection and criticism of the world.[5]

"Copernicus and Faustus in one", that is how Newton appeared to Keynes after he had examined these papers, which had remained so long hidden from men's sight. René Dugas, commenting on this passage, suggests another com-

[5] Lord Keynes, "Newton, the Man", in *Newton Tercentenary Celebrations* (published for the Royal Society by the Cambridge University Press, 1947), pp. 27–8.

parison: "Newton is a Pascal whose thoughts we do not know."

If we accept this account of the celebrated scientist—and it is admirably confirmed by the portrait painted by Godfrey Kneller[6] at the time Newton was writing the *Principia*—the text of the *Scholium generale* and that of the *Optics* have a very different ring about them. The following lines in particular seem to me very significant for our understanding of Newton's inner attitude:

> This Being governs all things, not as the soul of the world, but as Lord over all; and on account of his dominion he is wont to be called "Lord God" παντοκράτωρ, or "Universal Ruler"; for "God" is a relative word and has a respect to servants; and Deity is the dominion of God, not over his own body, as those imagine who fancy God to be the soul of the world, but over servants.... It is the dominion of a spiritual being which constitutes a God; ... it follows that the true God is a living, intelligent, and powerful Being.[7]

Newton's dependence upon God to account for the universal attraction which gives the universe its unity and regulates its parts does not therefore exhaust his concept of the nature of God. For Newton, God is above all *a person who reigns over persons*, and the latter's basic attitude towards him is one of *submission*.

We can scarcely doubt, therefore, that this was in fact Newton's own attitude. Did he not give glory to God, as Kepler had done, for his discovery of universal attraction and then, as time went on, for his deeper understanding of this principle and for the applications which he increasingly made possible?

His tragedy was that the impression produced on him by the sovereignty of the divine person became an obstacle in his

---

[6] The portrait is reproduced in the Royal Society's *Tercentenary Celebrations*, facing p. xvi.

[7] "General Scholium", in *Newton's Philosophy of Nature*, pp. 42–3.

thought, strained to the uttermost as it was, to the humble acceptance of the mystery of the Trinity. Newton believed he could only render complete homage to God by denying the faith of his baptism.

Einstein, with the immense sweep of his genius and the new picture he has given us of the universe, thanks to his discovery of the interdependence of the concepts of time, space and matter, belongs to the same lineage as Kepler and Newton. But does his avowed agnosticism allow us to include him with them as far as a religious view of the universe is concerned? We shall see that the answer to this question must be "Yes", but on condition that we specify those characteristics of Einstein's view of the universe which differentiate it from that of his predecessors.

What impressed Newton most, namely, the sovereignty of the divine person, is what Einstein found most repugnant. The chief reason for this repugnance must be sought in his way of life. The dominant force in Einstein's personality was quite simply his *independence of character*. The most obvious sign of this independence was his determination to free himself as far as possible from the conventions and constraints of life in society. At a deeper level, it accounts for his instinctive distrust of all generally accepted teaching and of the opinions prevailing in the circles among which he moved.

In fact, this is what made it possible for him to look at the universe and its problems in a way that was always new. He saw them with the eye of an astonished child, of the child he himself was, when at the age of five, he was wrapt in thought as he looked at a little mariner's compass his father had given him. Hence his respect for the mystery of the universe. This was the only religion whose credentials he recognized and which he wanted to see go hand in hand with science. Other religions he accused of seeking in the doctrine of a personal God a source of fear and hope, a fear capable of

restraining disordered appetites or the upsurge of violence, a
hope for the weak and the disinherited of this world. According to him, deliverance from the chains and the desires of
egoism is found in thoughts, feelings and aspirations *that have
a supra-personal value* and which, therefore, there is no need
to connect with any particular person, even a person whose
essence is divine.

Among these supra-personal values, the highest in Einstein's
view is *the intelligibility of the universe*, that is, the possibility of the discovery of the laws which prove verifiable and
operative in the sphere of experience and also show themselves as capable in the realm of thought of forming a rational
sequence which confers upon them an intrinsic consistency.

The search for these laws, which constitutes the task of the
scientist, presupposes in the latter a prior belief in the intelligibility of the universe as understood in this sense, and
comparable with *a genuine religious faith*:

> I cannot conceive of a genuine scientist without that pro-
> found faith. The situation may be expressed by an image:
> science without religion is lame, religion without science is
> blind.[8]

This cosmic religion was extolled by Einstein soon after his
arrival in the United States, in an article published by the *New
York Times* and reprinted on several subsequent occasions.
Here is an extract:

> I maintain that cosmic religious feeling is the strongest and
> noblest incitement to scientific research. Only those who realize
> the immense efforts and, above all, the devotion which pioneer
> work in theoretical science demands, can grasp the strength of
> the emotion out of which alone such work, remote as it is from
> the immediate realities of life, can issue. What a deep convic-
> tion of the rationality of the universe and what a yearning to

[8] Albert Einstein, in a symposium on Science, Philosophy and
Religion, printed in *Readings in the Philosophy of Science*, ed. P. P.
Wiener (Charles Scribner's Sons, New York, 1953), p. 605.

understand, were it but a feeble reflection of the mind revealed in this world, Kepler and Newton must have had to enable them to spend years of solitary labour in disentangling the principles of celestial mechanics! Those whose acquaintance with scientific research is derived chiefly from its practical results easily develop a completely false notion of the mentality of the men who, surrounded by a sceptical world, have shown the way to those like-minded with themselves, scattered through the earth and the centuries. Only one who has devoted his life to similar ends can have a vivid realization of what has inspired these men and given them the strength to remain true to their purpose in spite of countless failures. It is cosmic religious feeling that gives a man strength of this sort.[9]

This enthusiastic and almost religious confidence, which Einstein assures us he felt throughout his amazing career, has astonished more than one of those who knew him, accustomed as they were to hearing his sceptical and waggish remarks. Yet there is no contradiction here, for his acid criticisms were directed against what seemed to him a misunderstanding and an abuse of genuine religious awareness. And this abuse he often attributed to vested interests.

He explained this point of view in two letters to one of his best friends, Maurice Solovine:

I have never found a better expression than "religious" for faith in the rational nature of reality, which is thus, at least to a certain degree, accessible to human reason. Where this faith is lacking, science degenerates into a mechanical, rule-of-thumb business. And if the priests care to make capital out of this, let them!

You find it strange that I think of the comprehensibility of the world (so far as we are entitled to speak of such a comprehensibility) as a miracle or an external mystery. But surely, *a priori*, we should expect the world to be chaotic, not to be

[9] Albert Einstein, *The World as I See It*, trans. Alan Harris (Corvici and Friede, New York, 1934; John Lane, The Bodley Head, London, 1935), pp. 27–8.

grasped by thought in any way. We might (indeed, we *should*) expect that the world would be subject to law only so far as we impose order on it by our intelligence. This would be a sort of order like the alphabetical order of words in a dictionary. On the other hand, the kind of order created, for example, by Newton's gravitational theory is quite different. Even if the axioms of the theory are posited by man, the *success* of such a theory supposes in the objective world a high degree of order which we are decidedly not entitled to expect *a priori*. That is the "miracle", more and more evident as our knowledge develops.

And here is the weak point of positivists and professional atheists, who feel happy because they think that they have not only cleared the world finally and successfully of the gods but also "exposed all miracles". The strange thing is that we have to be satisfied with recognizing the "miracle" without having any legitimate way of getting any further. I have to add the last point explicitly, in case you think that I am so weakened by age that I have fallen into the hands of the priests.[10]

There is no need to take offence at the anticlerical remarks at the end of these two letters; their mischievous tone is typical of Einstein. Far from weakening the force of his reasoning, they strengthen it by revealing the independence and depth of his conviction, which was not shaken by the fear of finding himself associated with a proselytism which he abhorred.

What then was lacking in this reasoning to prevent it from reaching, beyond miracle, him who is its author? What in Einstein's thinking was the obstacle which hid from him the true image of the Creator? By refusing to accept the doctrine of a personal God, he meant to do away with the power of a will external to his own. The very notion of personality seemed to him essentially linked with a shutting out of other people. "I have never belonged", he said of himself, "with all my heart to one country or one state, nor to a circle of friends,

[10] Albert Einstein, *Lettres à Maurice Solovine* (Paris, 1956), pp. 103, 115.

nor even to my own family." Opposition between persons was, in his view, the source of all conflicts. To these only a will to power could put an end by imposing itself on others by threats or promises. This was the image of God which he refused to accept.

Einstein did not suspect that although the universe has its mysterious side God also has his and that a divine person does not allow himself to be measured by the limited or inaccurate standard with which our own personality provides us. He had to cross the threshold of eternity before he could see that creation is a work of love, before he, the technician of measurement, could see that God is immeasurable love.

From our preceding study of the religious view of the universe held by three great scientists belonging to the period of the renaissance of science, to its classical era and to modern times, there emerges one common characteristic which distinguishes it explicitly from the ancient or medieval view.

For the Greeks, the stellar world was of a different essence from our own. While the materials of which the earth is composed, and the beings who live in it, are subject to constant change affecting not only their situation relative to one another but also their own inner structure, the universe of the stars offered a spectacle of amazing permanence. Not only were their light and heat constant, but also the regularity of their movements. That of the fixed stars, and these were by far the most numerous, was also the simplest since it was no more than a uniform rotation round a single axis. The movement attributed to the sun and the planets was more complex, yet it could be reduced to a combination of various circular movements, and this combination was repeated periodically yet with no change whatever.

This character of changelessness in the heavens convinced men that these were eternal. Where and why should there be any end to the succession of cycles involving the sum total of the movements of the universe above the earth? What final catastrophe could be imagined when nothing seemed subject to change apart from the indefinitely recurring journey represented by circular trajectories accurately interlocked? To the infinity of duration was added the immensity of the space in which the stars moved. Even supposing that both their number and their distance from one another were finite, yet both of these were such that the sidereal universe seemed out of all proportion to the terrestrial world.

Apart from offering itself to man's contemplation, this universe allowed no possibility of access to it or of action upon it, and was obviously unknowable in its intrinsic nature.

It was precisely this disproportion between heaven and earth which was the source of the religious view of the ancient world. Whether the whole universe had been created, as the Bible taught, by God, as the artist gives birth to his work of art in his imagination before it takes shape in bronze or marble, or whether God was, as Plato thought, only a demiurge putting order into a world whose pre-existent parts had previously been endowed with no more than a chaotic form of being, the disproportion between heaven and earth led men to reflect on that existing between God and man, between God's knowledge and our ignorance, and from this reflection was spontaneously born an admiration mingled with respect and with fear.

As evidence of this, we need only reread in the thirty-eighth chapter of Job the first speech allotted by the author to Yahweh in order to impel Job to bow down before the divine transcendence. A few verses will suffice to convey the general tone:

Where wast thou when I laid the foundations of the earth?
Tell me if thou hast understanding.
Who hath laid the measures thereof, if thou knowest?
Or who hath stretched the line upon it?

Shalt thou be able to join together the shining stars the
 Pleiades,
Or canst thou stop the turning about of Arcturus?
Canst thou bring forth the day star in its time,
And make the evening star to rise upon the children of the
 earth?
Dost thou know the order of heaven,
And canst thou set down the reason thereof on the earth?

(Job 38. 3–4, 31–4.)

Ignorance of the laws of the heavens which, so it was supposed, were totally different from those governing terrestrial
phenomena, and the limits of man's knowledge of the latter,
these were the motives invoked to invite Job to respect the
mystery in which God clothes himself.

With the rapid growth of astronomical science from the
sixteenth century onward, all the frontiers between celestial
and terrestrial physics disappeared. Man no longer marvels,
as he faces the universe, at what he does not know, but at
what he succeeds in finding out, thanks to the union between mathematical thought and a technical equipment
revolutionized by the astronomical telescope. Mathematical
thought in particular, immaterial in nature and possessing the
power to unify the laws governing the solar system, is seen as
a gift of God and a reflection of his mode of knowledge.

This is why we find in Kepler and Newton, who never cast
any doubt on the existence of God, admiration and gratitude
for what he allows us to see of his power, and for his con-
descension in permitting us to penetrate in part his creative
thought.

Behind the cloud which conceals from him the true sense of
God's personality, there still remains in Einstein astonishment
mingled with respect before a mystery he finds incompre-
hensible, but which—by a paradox bordering on contradiction
—consists precisely in the fact that the scientist can compre-
hend the universe.

Christianity cannot remain indifferent to this change of perspective, thanks to which those who grope their way to God are now led towards him, no longer only by the spectacle offered to the senses by the stellar world and the impression of immensity which emerges from it and gives them a sense of their own insignificance, but by the ever increasing knowledge of it which is acquired by man's intellect in which there is reflected an image of the divine thought.

It should be remembered that Pius XII, in several speeches, passages from which I have already quoted, praised the recent discoveries of the astronomers and expressed his sincere admiration for the human mind's work of investigation, which is an excellent way by which to move upward to God.

CHAPTER VII

THE LAWS OF MOVEMENT AND THE DIVINE PERFECTIONS: DESCARTES TO MAUPERTUIS

"Theological mechanicalism" as we defined it at the beginning of the previous chapter did not limit itself to the general assertion of the mathematical intelligibility of the universe on the strength of laws and theories which reveal to us both the structure of the universe and the plan of the creative intelligence. Its advocates believed they could substantiate particular given laws by seeing them as witnessing to given particular divine perfections: immutability, universal causality, power or wisdom. Such an undertaking was bound to run a double risk, as we shall shortly see, namely, an anthropomorphic concept of God and an inaccurate estimation of the epistemological significance of the laws to which they appealed.

Descartes was the first to provide a complete statement of the principle of inertia. This he did by explicitly including two elements which were distinct and at the same time connected, namely, the conservation in time of the speed of a body moving in a vacuum together with the maintenance of the direction of its motion in a straight line.

Previously, and from the fourteenth century onward, physicists had seen the possibility of the conservation of motion, but in a circular path as well as a rectilinear one. A millstone continued to turn on its axis after it had been set in motion and left to move of its own accord. Why, asked Buridan, may we not explain in the same way the circular motion of the stars which would thus have been communicated to them initially by the Creator?

The question then arises as to how the privilege of a rectilinear movement can be justified by a similar reference to God. Descartes made the following attempt:

> God keeps every single thing in being by a continuous act and hence not as it may have been some time before, but just as it is at the very instant in which he is keeping it in being. Now of all movements, the rectilinear alone is wholly simple and its whole nature is comprised in one moment ... whereas, in order to conceive of circular movement, or any other sort whatsoever, we must consider at least two of these moments, or rather two of these parts and the relationship that exists between them (Descartes, *Le Monde*, ch. VII, Adam and Tannery edition (Paris, 1909), XI, pp. 44–5).

If we are to understand the thought of Descartes, which as stated here seems to contradict the axiom defining a straight line as the shortest distance between two points, we have to suppose that the philosopher had in mind, as he wrote these words, the tangent of an arc as then defined, that is, as a straight line having only one point in common with an arc at a given place and not cutting through the arc at this point. The uniqueness of the tangential point implies also that of the moment at which the moving body passes this point. In order to define the curvature in a given part of the arc we must determine two points on this arc and describe a tangent at each. It is the angle formed by the two tangents which is used to define the curvature. This makes Descartes's thought clear and also his concept of instantaneous movement which can only be rectilinear.[1]

This interpretation becomes still clearer as a result of Descartes's solution to another difficulty arising in his system from the denial of the possibility of a vacuum. How can the principle of inertia be applied if one of the conditions, formally enunciated in his definition, can never be realized?

The solution to this problem consists in breaking down any curvilinear movement into a succession of instantaneous movements which can be considered as taking place at each point in the arc in the direction of the tangent at this point, and this direction is, in any case, continuously variable.

With singular audacity, Descartes transfers this geometrical breaking down to the metaphysical realm of causality, by distinguishing, in the production of movement, the simultaneous intervention of two causes, God and created agents. While God gives to every moving body at each moment its existence, its state of motion and, in particular, the direction of this motion along the tangent to the curve of its path, created agents are responsible for the variation in velocity both as regards its absolute value and its direction. Here are Descartes's own words:

> Therefore ... we must say that God alone is the author of all movements in the universe in so far as they exist and in so far as they are rectilinear; but that they are made irregular or curvilinear by the diverse dispositions of matter. As the theologians teach us that God is also the author of all our actions in so far as they exist and have some good in them, but that

[1] Today we are more exacting and we define a tangent as the limit of the successive positions of a secant whose points of contact with the arc are considered to approach one another indefinitely, one being fixed and the other mobile. The uniqueness of the tangential point is thus reconciled with the fact that there are two points, the necessary condition for the definition of a straight line.

they are rendered evil by the divers dispositions of our wills . . .
(*Loc. cit.*, pp. 46–7).

From a strictly mechanist standpoint, the Cartesian analysis
of curvilinear movement is not lacking in interest, and the
Newtonian idea of force is founded upon it. But the distribution he made between divine action and the action of material
causes, as though God were playing at marbles and found
himself disturbed at every instant of the game, constitutes a
total misunderstanding of the difference between the act of the
first cause and that of the secondary causes. The only excuse
that can be found for Descartes lies in the taste his contemporaries had for theological discussions and the confused
memories of the scholastic exercises in which he doubtless
took part at La Flèche.

Another attempt at this kind of argument from the divine
perfections is concerned with the law by which Descartes
completes the principle of inertia, applicable to the movement
of a single moving body free from all outside influence. He
asserts the conservation of the sum of the quantities of motion
of the bodies meeting one another and modifying each other's
state of motion. This conservation of the total quantity of
motion, which Descartes without turning a hair extends to the
whole universe, results according to him,

from the sole fact of God's immutability, for, as he acts always
in the same way, he always produces the same effect. If we
suppose that he has put a certain quantity of motion into the
totality of matter in general from the first moment of its
creation by him, then we must admit that he always maintains
this quantity, or else cease to believe that he always acts in the
same way. If we also suppose that from that first moment, the
various parts of matter in which these motions found themselves unequally dispersed, began to keep them within themselves or else to transfer them from one to another, according
to what power they had to do so, then we must necessarily

think that he makes them always continue to act in the same way (*loc. cit.*, p. 43).

This so-called proof is full of gratuitous assertions. God's immutability would be still better guaranteed if nothing in the universe moved at all. Once motion is posited, it is more easily explained by the ancient concept of a stellar universe in which the stars maintain indefinitely the same motions along the same paths.

Once we have admitted the existence of motion proper to the stars nearest to us, it would be more in keeping with the divine immutability to suppose that the stars individually maintain the same velocities without having any effect upon one another. But this does not appear to be true on the galactic scale. Finally, if we admit that bodies meet and so modify one another, why should we hold that the divine immutability involves the permanence of the precise quantity defined by Descartes as the "quantity of motion" rather than that of any other quantity our experience or our reasoning can determine, without claiming to impose *a priori* our views on the divine thought?

But there is a still more serious objection. The law of the conservation of the quantity of motion, *as enunciated by Descartes*, that is by applying it to the *arithmetical sum* of the product of the mass of each body multiplied by its absolute speed, is erroneous. And this mistake involves the falsity of almost all the laws of impact accepted by Descartes. The exact law, which is expressed by replacing the sum in question by a vector sum, is itself for us today only one of the consequences of a theorem deduced from the simultaneous application of the principle of inertia and the Newtonian principle of the equality of action and reaction.

Its experimental verification confirms the possibility of rationally deducing the various laws of mechanics from a small number of general principles. It is nothing more—but also nothing less—than evidence in favour of what we have called "the intelligibility of the universe".

In 1686, thirty-six years after the death of Descartes, Leibniz in his *Acta eruditorum*, published at Leipzig, began a sharp criticism of the law enunciated by Descartes concerning the conservation of the quantity of motion. The title of the article, translated from the Latin, reads: "A short proof of a noteworthy error on the part of Descartes and other scientists, touching the so-called natural law by virtue of which God is supposed always to preserve the same quantity of motion. They make a wrong use of this law even in mechanics."

Leibniz's criticism did not attack the exact point at which the Cartesian law was false and required rectification. This correction was provided independently by Huygens and Malebranche. It involved substituting a different expression for that defined by Descartes as the "quantity of motion". This expression, called by Leibniz "active force", was the product of the multiplication of the mass of each body not by the absolute speed of the body but by its square.

In order to justify the introduction of this new expression and to show the Cartesians that his definition was superior to theirs, Leibniz had at his disposal an excellent *argumentum ad hominem*. Descartes in his efforts to account for the laws of equilibrium in such mechanisms as the lever, the pulley, the winch, etc., had shown that, if we imagine a very slight displacement of the weight which it is assumed is kept in balance by the machine, then a certain quantity must remain invariable. It is obtained by multiplying each force acting on the weight by the displacement imagined, this displacement being estimated *in the line of the force*; the products thus obtained are then added together.

Leibniz ingeniously began with this principle, which he assumed as generally admitted, and generalized the problem by asking what happens when the equilibrium is upset, as in the case of the fall of a body suddenly deprived of support. Or more precisely, what expression (here arrived at by finding the product of the mass of the moving body and its speed) must we have in mind so that the variation is *equivalent to that of the quantity considered by Descartes*, which we now call *work*?

On the strength of the laws of falling bodies, as enunciated by Galileo and admitted by all, Leibniz had no difficulty in showing that this quantity must be formed by multiplying the mass of the moving body by the square of its speed. Logically, the Cartesian principle of the *conservation of work* inevitably led to the analogous principle of the *conservation of active forces*.

Leibniz's little paper inaugurated a dispute between his followers and those of Descartes, the "active forces" quarrel. It lasted for fifty years. It is impossible to go into it here. What interests us is that Leibniz used the same metaphysical arguments as Descartes in order to impose his point of view. He had no hesitation in asserting that if, when two bodies met, there was no conservation of the sum total of active forces, the resultant confusion would not only be in our minds but in God himself.

Leibniz was able in the course of his brilliant career to make other contributions to mechanics. They were of unequal merit, but always inspired by the ingenuous conviction that a new aspect of the divine government of the universe had been brought to light. Two years before his death, in 1716, he wrote the following explanation in his *Principles of Nature and of Grace*:

> God's supreme wisdom has made him choose especially *those laws of motion* which are most adapted to and most appropriate for abstract or metaphysical reasoning. So the quantity of total, absolute, force, or action is constant; the quantity of respective force, or reaction, is constant; and the quantity of the directive force is constant. Further, action

is always equal to reaction, and the total effect always equivalent to its total cause. And it is surprising that we cannot account for these laws of movement, discovered in our time and some of them by myself, by merely considering *the efficient causes* or matter. For I have found that it is necessary to proceed to *the final causes* and that these laws do not depend on the *principle of necessity* as do logical, arithmetical and geometrical truths, but on *the principle of appropriateness*, that is, on the choice made by wisdom. And this is one of the most telling and cogent proofs of the existence of God for those who are capable of penetrating reality.

The arbitrary character of this appeal to the divine perfections is fully revealed in the long controversy carried on by letter between Leibniz and Clarke, who acted as secretary to Newton. While Clarke appealed to divine providence and to God's free government of the universe, Leibniz attempted to bind God by the principle of sufficient reason and thus set himself up as the only qualified interpreter of the divine decisions.

Beneath this apparently philosophical discussion there was a scarcely concealed struggle on the part of each to extend his own sphere of influence, and also Leibniz's bitter disappointment at seeing Newton preferred to him by his former protector, George Louis of Hanover, who had become king of England in 1714.

I shall not return to Newton's religious thought, which I described in the last chapter. But it is as well to add a few particulars regarding the apologetic value which Newton and his disciples saw in the principle of universal attraction. According to Cartesian mechanicalism, matter, whose essence is reduced to extension, can only be passive, and if the motion initially imparted to it by God can, as Descartes insisted, be communicated from one body to another, this can only be through the contact achieved by impact. Where this contact is not visible to our sight, for instance in the case of a falling body, we must come to the rescue of the weakness of our senses and assert the existence of a subtle form of matter, through whose agency movement is transmitted.

In opposition to this notion and because of their respect for experience, which assures us of the existence of an (at least relatively) empty space between solid bodies, the Newtonians taught that universal attraction had been superadded by direct act of God, following on the creation of matter which had already taken place. Its real existence, confirmed by its many consequences which our calculations make it possible for us to deduce, constituted a proof of God's existence and revealed the character of his providential government.

This thesis is developed by Roger Cotes in the preface which he wrote for the second edition of the *Principia*:

> All sound and true philosophy is founded on the appearances of things; and if these phenomena inevitably draw us, against our wills, to such principles as most clearly manifest to us the most excellent counsel and supreme dominion of the All-wise and Almighty Being, they are not therefore to be laid aside because some men may perhaps dislike them. These men may call them miracles or occult qualities, but names maliciously given ought not to be a disadvantage to the things themselves, unless these men will say at last that all philosophy ought to be founded in atheism.[2]

As Mme Metzger remarks, the spiritual philosophies of both Descartes and Newton are founded on a duality in primordial realities. But the opposition between *extended substance* and *thinking substance* was succeeded by the duality of *inert matter* and *attractive force*. In both cases, this spiritual philosophy rests on ignorance; in the case of Descartes, of the way mind acts upon matter, in the case of Newton, of the relation between inertia and attraction.

The rational link which was missing at the time when the Newtonian concepts were first elaborated appears in Ein-

[2] *Newton's Philosophy of Nature*, p. 133.

stein's theory of gravitation. Inertia and attraction are two aspects, varying according to the state of the observer's movement, of one single reality, the curvature of space-time itself due to the existence and distribution of the matter it contains.

We may conclude with Mme Metzger:

> Once this dualism (of inertia and attraction) which from the aesthetic point of view may be considered a blemish, ceases to exist, the natural theology derived from Newtonianism falls completely to pieces and we are left with a physics which can do without theological considerations and a religion which is wholly freed from the ascendancy of metaphysics. And each is independent of the other.

Although he followed Leibniz in reflecting on *final causes*, Maupertuis was not satisfied with general statements concerning the laws of mechanics as a whole. He did not even hold that it was possible to state these laws in the form of *principles of conservation*. The characteristic feature of his contribution to the science of mechanics is his notion of reducing to a single formula the laws both of equilibrium and of motion, and his formulation of this one law as a *minimum principle* in the sense of a *principle of economy*.

Further, the *principle of least action* revealed a new quantity, *action* which may be considered as a synthesis of the Cartesian *quantity of motion* and Leibniz's *active force*. The quantum theory was later to show its importance.

Let us take a material point of mass m, whose velocity v varies along the path followed, solely in relation to its position along the path it follows. If, after dividing the path between two given points A and B into the elements ds, we calculate from A to B the sum of the infinitesimal products $\int mvds$, this sum—now known as the *Maupertuisian action*—calculated for the *path actually followed* by the moving body between A and B, is *smaller* than for any other path traced between the same two points. This is how Maupertuis enunciated the principle known as that of "least action".

Its author rightly insisted on the greater degree of accuracy he had brought to the definition of *action*, and also on the *form of the principle*, in which he saw the mark of divine wisdom, which however did not dispense the scientist from having recourse to the calculus; a calculus, moreover, of a special kind, the *calculus of variations*, which was considerably developed later by Euler and Lagrange.

As for the metaphysical interpretation of the principle of least action, Maupertuis wrote as follows in a memorandum read to the Paris Academy of Sciences in 1744:

> We cannot doubt that all things are ruled by a supreme Being who, while he has imprinted upon matter forces which denote his power, has destined them to produce effects which show his wisdom. The harmony of these two attributes is so perfect that doubtless all the phenomena of nature could be deduced from each taken in isolation. A blind and determined mechanics follows the designs of the most enlightened and the most free intelligence. If our mind were comprehensive enough, it would also see the causes of the physical effects, either by calculating the properties of bodies, or by seeking to discover what is the most appropriate means to produce effects from these causes.
>
> The first of these methods is more within our scope than the second, but it does not get us very far. The second sometimes leads us astray because we have insufficient knowledge of the end nature has in view, and because we may be mistaken in regard to the *quantity* which we must consider as its *expenditure* in the production of its effects. If our researches are to have breadth as well as reliability, we must use both methods. Let us calculate the movements of bodies, but let us also investigate the designs of the intelligence which causes them to move.

This remarkable passage reveals the anxiety of its author not to fall back into the exaggerations and errors of his predecessors and so to use simultaneously mathematical method and metaphysical reflection while taking care that each acted as a check on the other.

If Maupertuis had been content to talk of *deductive* and *inductive* method—the latter consists in anticipating the results checked by the former, by bringing to light *analogies* existing between phenomena of different sorts, or even analogies borrowed from more trivial considerations such as the desire not to multiply explanations—there would be nothing to object to in his wise and prudent counsels. But we find that he too suffers from the prevalent disorder of the philosophy of his time, namely an ambition to give absolute value to the humble work of human research by attributing the same mentality to God.

In regard to the *form* of the principle of least action, Lagrange dispelled the illusion by successively showing, first that the so-called principle was no more than a *theorem* which could be proved on the basis of the general laws of motion; then that the so-called *minimum* of Maupertuisian action might quite equally be a *maximum*, for the essential requirement for an infinitely small change in the path between two given fixed points is that the variation of the integral defining Maupertuisian action should be *nil*. This is why Maupertuis's principle is generally known today as the "principle of stationary action".

These two observations of Lagrange reduced the *metaphysical reflection* and the *inquiry into God's designs* as proposed by Maupertuis to a simple *epistemological reflection* on the application to mechanics of the method used in the calculus of variations.

Lagrange's *Mécanique analytique*, the first edition of which dates from 1788, marks the final point in the development of the attempt to treat in a purely rational way all the branches of mechanics: statics, hydrostatics, dynamics and hydrodynamics.

Not that the author systematically ignores the work of his predecessors. On the contrary, the precious historical notes, with which he has enriched his treatise, bear witness to his immense erudition and to the objectivity of his judgements. But his own work is one of systematization by the *use of algebraic calculation alone*. In the Foreword, he wrote:

> No diagrams will be found in this book. The methods I put forward require no geometrical or mechanical constructions or reasoning, but only algebraical operations in strict and uniform progression. Those who have a fondness for analysis will be pleased to see mechanics as its new branch, and will be grateful to me for having thus extended its scope.

Lagrange's *Mécanique analytique* is a work dealing with history, science and the philosophy of science, and it opens the way to a strictly rational conception of mechanics.

As for the different principles whose history we have re-called in the present chapter, Lagrange endeavoured to determine their real bearing and to show their dependence on one another. In the process, he stripped them of all meta-physical and theological meaning by dispelling an illusion that had lasted only too long.

This certainly does not mean that Lagrange succeeded in cutting off mechanics completely from its original links with the investigation of machines. In order to justify the principle of virtual work, not evident enough in his view to posit, as Descartes had done, as a first principle, he preferred to connect it with what he called the *principle of pulleys*.

It is always possible in fact, however complex the problem of equilibrium whose solution is being sought, to replace the forces in action by the traction of ropes having the necessary tension and returned in the appropriate directions by means of a combination of fixed or mobile pulleys and the action of a single weight. The Cartesian principle is then seen as a simple consequence of the well-known principle of Torricelli, according to which an infinitely small displacement of the system will not take place unless it allows the tensor weight to move downward.

Pulleys and ropes, that is, the assimilation of a force, whatever its origin, to a rope held taut by a weight; the intellectual honesty of the great algebraist considered it wrong to conceal this appeal to the concrete and we must be grateful to him for his honest recognition of the fact.

For us Christians the image of a pulley and a rope recalls to our memory Christ himself sitting on the edge of Jacob's well and showing his interest in the familiar movement of the woman of Samaria who had come there to draw water. We know how our Lord beginning with this movement and this water raised the thoughts of the woman towards the supernatural realities of grace.

Movements such as these, performed day by day in the knowledge of a duty accepted and done, were brushed aside as servile works by the aristocratic science of the Greeks and considered unworthy to occupy the thoughts of free citizens. But Christian wisdom interested itself in them and, in order to make them more easy to perform, applied itself to the search for the secret of their efficacy.

The generous act of rendering service thus made possible the birth of the *science of machines*, which the genius of scientists such as Lagrange later raised to the level of a science as rationalized as that of the Greeks; it is our modern science of *mechanics*. We do not deny that it remains human and imperfect and is not, any more than geometry, the manner in which the divine intellect operates. But Christ, sitting at the right hand of the Father, is interested in these humble processes, just as he was long ago in the work of the Samaritan woman. There is no reason to doubt that this science too may help the mind of the scientist, enlightened by the Spirit, to rise to the mysteries of the kingdom of God itself.

I bring this chapter and those which come before it to their conclusion by insisting that although it is useless to try to justify the principles of mechanics by theological views, as the scientists of the seventeenth and eighteenth centuries attempted to do, misunderstanding in the process both the divine transcendence and the experimental origins of a science which had emerged from the study of machines, nevertheless it is certain that Christian thought presided at the birth of this science by interesting itself in human work and in all possibilities of making it easier.

Those who evolved the theory of mechanics did no more than continue on strictly rational lines the reflections of technicians on elementary machines and ballistics. The Greeks, in spite of the timorous attempts of Archimedes, were not aware that such reflection was also a liberal discipline on a par with geometry. It is to the credit of the Christian Middle Ages to have understood that this was so.

PART III

PRESENT-DAY PROBLEMS

THE EVOLUTION OF SCIENCE FROM THE EIGHTEENTH TO THE NINETEENTH AND TWENTIETH CENTURIES

If we are to account for the attitude of Christianity towards science in our own times and to state the problems which face the Christian scientist today, we must take into consideration the evolution of science from the days of Newton as a consequence of the triumph of his ideas in Europe. At a time when astrophysics comprised merely a few data concerning the sun, the determination of the laws of the movement of the planets and their unification by the more general law of universal attraction gave the mind of man the power to grasp the *System of the Universe* at length unveiled before his eyes and henceforth stripped of all its mystery.

The hypothesis of molecular attraction obeying the same law and the application by Coulomb of a formula, identical with that of Newton, to electric and magnetic attraction, extended the laws of astronomy to the constitution of matter and communicated to the whole of our knowledge in the field of physics an impressive unity. The celebrated saying of Laplace concerning the determinism which governs the whole universe witnesses to this ingenuous confidence in the power and certainty of scientific knowledge which henceforth could abandon all recourse to metaphysics or to a theodicy. Hence the complete "secularization" of science which is seen as the work of the human mind at length delivered from all belief in an architect of the universe. Auguste Comte's law of the three states provided an attractive formula for this new freedom and opened the era of positivism.

This state of mind was still supreme at the beginning of the twentieth century. It had been strengthened by the triumph of the chemical atomic theory and the representation of the atom itself as a miniature planetary system.

This ingenuous and enthusiastic conception of the unity of science and the simplicity of the structure of the universe has received a setback during the twentieth century in the fields of theory and experiment.

In Newton's work two principal sections completed and confirmed one another. On the one hand were the general laws of dynamics, based on the principle of inertia and on that of the equality between action and reaction; on the other, were the notion of universal attraction and the formulation of its law.

But the theory of relativity has once more called in question these two complementary aspects of Newton's work. For the Newtonian dynamics, characterized by the invariability of the mass of material bodies, the special theory of relativity has substituted another, distinguished by the variation of mass in relation to velocity, the mass of a body increasing to infinity when its velocity approaches that of light. The general theory of relativity for its part has substituted for the idea of attraction operating at a distance between two stars, the distortion of the space-time continuum in the presence of matter and under its influence.

But the setback suffered by the notion of attraction is still more serious at the molecular and atomic level, and the quantum theory is more revolutionary than the theory of relativity. We know that its precise interpretation involves the uncertainty relations, discovered by Heisenberg, and that these relations contradict the Laplacian concept of determinism.

These new ideas have singularly modified the strict and absolute character of statements dealing with the scope of scientific laws. We now have to take into account the effect of the act of measurement upon the phenomena observed, and this is responsible for the problematical nature of predictions.

The success of the theories of relativity and of quantum mechanics is due in great part to the experimental verifications provided by two groups of techniques, those of astrophysics and of nuclear physics. The giant telescopes of Mount Wilson and Mount Palomar have revealed to us the extent of the world of the galaxies, and the spectroscope has made it possible to note their movement away from the earth, and so gives an effective content to the theory of expanding space. The accelerators of particles have enabled velocities to be reached that increasingly approximate to the speed of light and have made it possible to verify the accuracy of the formulae of relativity dynamics.

But experiment is not only the servant of theory, it goes beyond it and requires developments of which we have as yet no conception. This is the case with the discovery of the new particles and anti-particles which double those we already know. While the new concepts of matter and space go beyond Newton's and Leibniz's system of the universe, they themselves are outrun by the experimental discoveries which result from a revolutionized technique.

This evolution of theory and this extension of the field of experiment have produced a change of outlook among scientists. Science no longer seems to them a closed area in which there are now only certain details to be learnt, and the

systemization of the knowledge already acquired to be per-
fected. It is rather an adventure which is taking us we know
not whither, nor do we know what risks have to be run. New
problems are arising and we do not know how to master them.
Theory has not caught up with experiment.

Hence an attitude of humility which is in sharp contrast
to the pride of nineteenth-century science. The scientist
today is becoming conscious of the immensity of the field to
be explored and the moderate achievement we can claim, as
well as of the inadequacy of the concepts emerging from knowledge on the human plane, especially those of time, space and
causality, if we are to grasp reality on the level of the
infinitely great and the infinitely small.

By the same token there has been a lessening of the
opposition which, during the last century, set the men of
science against the men of faith. This was due to the fact that
the latter held that beyond the field of science, limited both as
regards its object and its methods, there were the fields of
philosophy and theology.

Today, in the universities, Christians and unbelievers are
found side by side and have nothing but mutual esteem for
one another, for the science of one group and the Christianity
of the other have taught them both the virtue of humility;
and they all face the same problems. Here is what one of them
has to say:

> Between Christian and non-Christian scientists in our times,
> there is a common denominator, composed of the corpus of
> knowledge, of all the qualities that must be developed if
> research is to be undertaken, and the attitude to be adopted
> towards the results of research and as regards science itself . . .
> an attitude of humility, of concern and anxiety, which is in
> singular contrast to that of the nineteenth century. We all have
> this same attitude. For those who have faith, it is written into
> their faith itself and at a very deep level. Yet it is equally
> present in those scientists who are not Christians. This is why

we get on perfectly well together. There is a sense of brotherhood which certainly did not exist in the nineteenth century, between those scientists who have a religious temperament and those who have not. In the past, there was a certain stiffness, an abrupt, unyielding, proud attitude which raised formidable barriers between us. But this is no longer the case. We discuss together the problems of life and death. These discussions are genuinely friendly and we genuinely respect one another's convictions, because we share the same forward-looking spirit and the same anxieties in face of the way the world is going.

These are the words of Louis Leprince-Ringuet in a public interview after one of the lectures during the *Rencontres Internationales de Genève* (1958) on the subject of man and the atom. This testimony is all the more valuable in that it is that of a qualified research worker, the leader of a team which has contributed to the increase of our knowledge of cosmic rays and the new particles. And this research worker openly professes his Christianity.

CHAPTER IX

THE AUTONOMY OF SCIENTIFIC METHOD AND THE RELIGIOUS PROBLEM

Some scientists profess Christianity, others are unbelievers; the scientific quality of the work of both has nothing to do with their attitude towards the religious problem. This is a fact that compels our recognition today, and the reference to L. Leprince-Ringuet has just shown us that the peaceful co-existence and collaboration of believing and unbelieving scientists in the field of their own special study are characteristic of the scientific world of the twentieth century. The reason for this must be sought in the method of work common to them all and in its autonomy as regards religion, Christianity in particular.

In the medieval period, all branches of human knowledge were interdependent and their unity was conceived on the pattern of a hierarchical order in the subjects they studied. Physics especially, that is the science of nature, was subordinated to metaphysics, the science of being as such. The task of physics was to inquire into the conditions under which being was subject to changes such as those revealed to us through observation of the sensible world by which we are surrounded. Physical science, according to this view, was a science of observation from which methodical experiment was almost completely absent. The phenomena observed were considered in all their complexity and thought to be precisely what sense knowledge revealed them to be as it delivered them to the operation of the mind.

Modern physics, on the contrary, analyses phenomena and seeks to determine the conditions under which they recur in an identical manner, and this for the purpose of discovering the laws governing this recurrence of identical phenomena and then of establishing connections between the newly discovered laws and those previously known. The discovery of these connections provides the explanation of phenomena recently studied by including them in a wider context that has already been acquired by the same method.

In order to reach these laws, it is first necessary to define the characteristic quantities of the phenomena studied, and then to proceed to the measurement of the values assumed by these quantities by varying the circumstances under which the phenomena are produced. Measurement provides a series of coded numbers and the interdependence of these series is expressed in mathematical functions which summarize the results of numerous measurements and are themselves the enunciation of the laws governing the production of phenomena that can be repeated under identical conditions.

The chemist proceeds by means of a method of analysis and repetition similar to that of the physicist. But instead of concentrating its attention on the phenomena, that is on the *movements* (to use the concepts of ancient physics), this method applies itself to what ancient physics called the *substances*, air, water, metals, etc. This analysis makes it possible to obtain pure substances whose properties are independent of the circumstances of the origin or the production of the given substances in the original experiment. The fact that these properties can recur is shown by measurements produced by a technique borrowed from the physicist, and is proof of the degree of purity obtained. Conversely, it is only by using pure substances that the physicist can obtain measurements that provide relations which can be made to recur in the most rigorous sense of the term. Modern physics, whether nuclear or semi-conductor, is absolutely insistent on the degree of purity it requires in the substances it obtains from the chemist.

The study of this modern scientific method shows that it is characterized by three major and essential factors—it insists on objectivity, intersubjectivity and rationality.

Its insistence on objectivity is revealed in the importance attached by modern science to measurements and the conditions under which these measurements are made and used.

At the outset, phenomenological description remains indispensable, and this is a point forgotten by some philosophers in whose view physics attempts to obtain quantity for its own sake and so is an essentially mathematical type of knowledge. However, science cannot remain purely qualitative without running the risk of introducing a subjective element which falsifies and sometimes even is wholly responsible for the creation of the so-called "observed" phenomenon.

That this proviso is necessary is shown by a story we are now inclined to forget, namely, the alleged discovery of N rays by Blondlot. This physicist, in all other respects enjoying the esteem of his fellow scientists, thought he had observed that a phosphorescent screen, previously sensitized by being exposed to light and then observed in darkness, received an increase of luminosity when certain objects were brought close to it or when certain phenomena were induced in its neighbourhood. He thought he was justified in attributing this increase of phosphorescence to a new form of radiation, N rays. After a period of enthusiasm during which N rays were found everywhere, the new discovery sank into profound oblivion when the suspicion arose, and was later confirmed, that it was due to an optical illusion. To become objective,

N rays needed a set of measuring instruments able to reveal their existence by studying the circumstances under which they were produced.

However, in taking a measurement with an appropriate set of measuring instruments, it is still possible for the observer to falsify the measurement without realizing it. This is known as the personal error. It occurred formerly in the observation of the image of a star on the focus of the object-glass of a transit instrument, when the position of the focus was determined merely by cross-hairs. Today the use of the so-called "impersonal" micrometer has made it possible to do away with the subjective visual influence of the operator.

In spite of these improvements, there are no perfect instruments, and insistence on objectivity leads to the correction of raw measurements to compensate for defects in the apparatus used.

Finally, the possible reaction, caused by the insertion of the measuring apparatus, on the phenomenon studied has to be neutralized. Thus in measuring the electric tension between two points on a network of conductors, a voltmeter is cut in between the points. It produces a new branching of the current which can cause a variation in the tension it is proposed to measure. Here again a correction is necessary.

As these few details show, the measuring operation proves that the wish to eliminate the influence of the observer and of what he does, from the objective study of phenomena, is far more obvious than the wish to apply mathematics to the object studied.

In spite of all the improvements in apparatus and notwithstanding the professional skill of the scientist who makes and corrects the measurements, errors are still possible. A hypothesis can only be free from them if several observers take measurements of the same quantity and, if possible, with different apparatus and even by different methods, and then reach the same results. This is what we have called the condition of intersubjectivity.

It is best realized today by team work, thanks to which the same phenomenon is dealt with by various observers using different methods and pooling the results obtained. We have only to read the reports of the scientific academies, etc., to see that today, by contrast with the nineteenth century, the majority of the papers are signed by several authors who have collaborated to produce the result they report.

Further, other teams study the same phenomena and criticize each other's work. It is from the continual comparison of their results and from their agreement on essentials that it is possible to reach an objective certainty from which all legitimate doubt is excluded. It is by this method in particular that a very precise determination of the fundamental quantities of physics has been obtained: the velocity of light, Planck's constant, the charge of the electron, etc.

This abundance of precautions in the effort to achieve objectivity in experimental method and to reach agreement among physicists might lead one to believe that quantitative measurements and the laws which bind them together constitute the final aim of scientific method. This is not so. According to the term which has become classic since Meyerson, the scientist seeks "explanation" or more accurately—and here we follow Bachelard—"rationality".

But there are many types of rationality. The rationality characteristic of the scientific method consists in the reduction of particular laws to a smaller number of general laws, for instance, the three laws of Kepler reduced to the law of universal attraction established by Newton, or again the reduction of several distinct classes of phenomena to one single all-inclusive class, for instance, Maxwell's reduction of optics to electro-magnetism and that of dynamics to electro-magnetism as achieved by Einstein.

In this search for unity, the scientist finds a powerful auxiliary in mathematical constructions. Thus the reduction of optics and then of dynamics to electro-magnetism was obtained, on the one hand, by Maxwell's equations, and on the other, by the use of Lorentz's transformation, which made more precise the conditions of invariance of Maxwell's equations in systems whose movement is relative, linear and uniform.

But these equations are only a means and not an end for the physicist, who is seeking to understand and who aims at a rational explanation. The twofold reduction we have just mentioned is based, in our opinion, on the existence of a limit of velocity that cannot be attained by any moving body which is the bearer of energy, and on the identification of this velocity with that of light. In other words, it is the interpretation given to the universal constant which ensures the intelligibility of optics and dynamics by linking them to the laws of electro-magnetism in which this constant plays an essential part.

Another means that makes it possible to reach rationality lies in the *analogies* between phenomena of different kinds but expressible in the same equations. Here again, the equations are not sought for their own sakes but because their identity leads to comparisons which make the phenomena studied intelligible. Thus, in the study of mechanical or electric oscillations, the comparison between self-induction and inertia, between the part played by condensers and that played by springs, makes it possible to rationalize the mechanism generating oscillations, since it can be made independent of the material aspect of the phenomena. In Gaston Bachelard's book there are very well-chosen and well-developed examples which illustrate this aspect of the rational character of physics.

The brief resumé of the scientific method we have just given, especially as it is practised in physics, shows clearly enough that it is independent of metaphysics and even, though to a lesser extent, of mathematics, in the sense that the physicist does not attempt to discover quantity for its own sake, but as the most suitable means of obtaining both objectivity and rationality in his knowledge, which remains in the experimental order and aims to explore the material universe to its furthest bounds, the galaxies and the interior of the atom.

It is clear that this method rests on a choice, namely, that of the relations that can recur in identical conditions. It therefore leaves quite to one side the universe of persons, since the latter is in fact formed of what is not repeatable, for each person brings to the sum total of other persons his own originality and his own irreplaceable contribution.

A metaphysics centred on the notion of the person enjoys a total autonomy in regard to positive science. It is nevertheless true that the physicist is himself a person and so the physical and the metaphysical in him cannot be completely ignorant of one another. This is still more the case with biology and the so-called social sciences.

Scientific method enjoys a similar autonomy in regard to Christianity and more generally, in relation to the religious problem. Religion is in fact essentially a relationship of the person of man and the person of God. And Christianity, as we have already noted, is a history of salvation. Christ came into the world to be its Saviour, as the angels proclaimed on the day of his birth. The idea of the salvation or of the loss of the soul remains outside the scientific method.

Hence the investigator as such remains free to accept or not to accept the salvation wrought by Christ, to believe or to refuse to believe in his message, to seek or to renounce personal relations with God. His choice will not affect the quality of his scientific work. On the other hand, this choice, in so far as it is free, that is, independent of all family or social pressure, will not hinder in any way his task of investigation.

The free character of the act of faith has always been

asserted by Christianity, since this freedom is the necessary condition of merit. The act however constitutes a duty for the Christian who is enlightened as regards his religion. This should be evidence enough that there cannot be any opposition between Christianity and science. The only real problem regarding their relationship lies within the person of the scientist himself, for it remains for him to harmonize his free following of Christ and his professional activity as an investigator in a given scientific field.

CHAPTER X

HARMONY BETWEEN THE SPIRIT OF FAITH AND THE SPIRIT OF RESEARCH

The freedom of the investigator in regard to the religious problem is not only a freedom to which he is entitled since it is founded on the autonomy of scientific method, it is also today an actual freedom expressed by the coexistence of two contrary currents of thought among scientists. Yet it must be recognized that Christian scientists do experience difficulties in harmonizing in their lives the spirit of faith and the spirit of research. These difficulties have been studied in an article by Paul Germain on the spiritual life of the research worker, in *Cahier* 4 of *Recherches et Débats*, and entitled *Pensée scientifique et foi chrétienne*; it was published in May 1953. I shall begin by examining these difficulties with a view to then seeing how it is possible to overcome them.

The first difficulty arises from the absorbing nature of scientific work which occupies the whole of a man's attention. We are no longer living in the days of the amateur, when the progress of science was in the hands of men in very varied social situations—ecclesiastics, magistrates, engineers, etc.— whose scientific work occupied the leisure time provided by their professions. Today research is itself a profession which has in many cases its own form of organization, as is the case in France thanks to the Centre National de la Recherche Scientifique. The grouping of research workers into teams emphasizes their mutual dependence and promotes a certain rivalry which focuses the efforts of each member upon the realization of the aim assigned to him.

The rapid increase of discoveries in newly worked fields (we need only think of macromolecules, the semi-conductor and above all nuclear energy) makes science a wonderful and fascinating adventure which involves not only the routine of daily work but even the life of the mind itself. On official holidays there are specially organized discussions between those who specialize in a given problem; qualified lecturers report on the present state of research, while exhibitions of technical apparatus whose ingenious methods and the appliances which work them can be admired and at the same time the creative imagination of those engaged in experiments is stimulated.

It is therefore easy to understand the difficulty Catholic scientists experience in maintaining the superiority of spiritual values and in living a genuine life of faith side by side with their active life as research workers. The same is true of the life of prayer which requires times for meditation and the minimum of contemplation parallel with the active life that is demanded of every Christian, since his supernatural vocation is to seek and to find God.

Other more specific obstacles exist in addition to this basic difficulty. They result from the habits of thought created in the scientist by the continual use of the scientific method. We may group them round the three characteristics of this method, namely, objectivity, intersubjectivity and rationality.

What degree of objectivity must we grant to the facts contained in the Gospel narrative, to miracles in particular? A mind formed by the scientific method will hesitate to accept them on the same grounds as the experimental facts verified in the laboratory. It will therefore be tempted to treat the Gospels as an article of faith. But the Gospel facts are for the Christian a motive of credibility, and the authenticity of the miracles has to be established prior to the act of faith, by a study based on the methods of history and not on those of physics.

The physicist, accustomed to arriving easily at agreement with his colleagues, will also be disturbed by the various interpretations of the sacred books which he finds among the different Christian denominations. He will also find it difficult to give to the traditional proofs of the existence of God the same rational value he discovers in a mathematical demonstration or in the validity of a system of equations representing a class of physical phenomena.

There is no point in disguising these difficulties or in minimizing them. The light of religious truth has not the impersonal and irrefutable nature of scientific truth. It does not force the believer's assent, it solicits it by leaving him free to accept or to refuse. On the other hand, the acceptance required is not of a purely intellectual kind, it is the acceptance not only of Christ's teaching, but of Christ himself as a person, by an engagement in which the person of the believer is also involved. It is in this sense that we have to understand and are able to justify Pascal's wager.

Perhaps, however, these difficulties may be lessened if we note that the irrefutable character of scientific truth is more apparent than real. It presupposes the admission of certain data which have been tacitly accepted for centuries, but which we now recognize are by no means obligatory on the mind. This is the case with the non-Euclidean geometries. A more topical example still is that of the axiom "the whole is greater than its parts", which is verified in the field of the finite, but not in that of the transfinite.

In spite of the intersubjectivity of which we have spoken, there are serious differences between scientists, for instance, in the interpretation of the mechanics of wave-motion. The idealist school, known as the "Copenhagen" school, is opposed by the realist school of Louis de Broglie, Bohm and Vigier. The Marxists themselves are divided on the genuine dialectical character of both positions.

Finally, since it is impossible for any scientist to master science as a whole and to have a personal conviction about every problem, it is obvious that only a faith in the authority acquired by certain specialists, and a purely human faith at that, can make it legitimate for scientists as a body to accept their conclusions. This faith in any case is reasonable and is based on serious motives of credibility whose value is established by a rigorous critique of the evidence.

Truth has many facets but they all have certain common features and the Christian knows that they are gathered together in the person of Christ who proclaimed that he himself was the truth. In spite of their dissimilarities, religious experience and physical experience are related, since both are founded on the common virtue of honesty, on respect due to facts, whether the latter are exterior to the soul of the believer or within it, whether they are natural or supernatural. It is no mere chance that Pascal, who reverenced experiment in the field of physics, has left us one of the finest witnesses to a religious experience of which we have authentic documentary evidence.

Yet we must follow Pascal in insisting on the transcendent character of Christianity and in accepting the fact that there is a state of tension in the Christian scientist between his science and his faith. The second is not just a mere extra added to the first. God does not bring a supplementary explanation, as Maupertuis thought, to be added to that given by the application of mathematics to physics. *A fortiori* God is not a mathematician, as Plato described him.

God is love and it is in the trusting acceptance of this love, however inordinate it may appear to us in the mystery of the Cross, that the act of faith consists. *Credidimus caritati*, St John tells us. The Christian is the man who believes in the love of God for the human race; he believes that this love has gone so far as to give him God's own Son.

If Pascal were to come back to life, he would tell us that all the galaxies that fill the heavens and increase the span of space cannot produce the least act of the intellect, and that all the knowledge accumulated by scientists since his experiment on the Puy-de-Dôme cannot produce the least act of charity for "that is of another and infinitely higher order".

To safeguard this transcendence of charity, the Christian scientist must make room in his work-life for times of prayer. Nothing can take the place of this awareness of the divine presence in the depths of our souls as baptized persons, nothing can take the place of this dialogue of the soul with its Creator. The times when we begin our principal tasks or when we change our occupations are moments that can provide the opportunity for this turning in upon ourselves, for this practice of the presence of God. Our difficulties too may do their part by causing us to call upon God to help us. This might even be the case with our technical difficulties, when we cannot immediately grasp the point of a proof, or when we are trying to find the reason for a failure after an experiment which does not give the result we expected. By lifting our eyes to God, by asking for the light of the Holy Spirit, we may then re- member that, in the last analysis, our work is destined to extend the kingdom of God in this world and that we should rely on his grace to enable us to be worthy workers for this cause.

It may help us to rise above the material nature of our daily tasks if we follow Pascal's scheme of the three orders and reflect on the work of the intellect in science. The study of scientific epistemology and of the history of science helps us to understand the part played by the development of science and technology in the vocation of man and prepare the mind for the subsequent discovery of the plan of Providence which has placed man on the earth with the mission to take possession of it and to subdue it by using the noblest of his faculties, and so to offer it in homage to God.

Finally, since charity towards our neighbour is the effective sign of our love of God, the Catholic research worker will be anxious to make a special effort to place himself at the disposal of his fellow workers. Team organization, which we have already mentioned, favours exchanges of services which may, as occasion arises, be followed by exchanges of views between research workers on matters which go beyond their immediate technical preoccupations and take their place in a philosophy of culture or even in a theology. Thus it seems to us possible, though difficult, to achieve that symbiosis between the spirit of faith and the spirit of research of which we gave examples in our Foreword by quoting from Pierre Termier and Fr Teilhard de Chardin.

CHAPTER XI

THE MOST UNIVERSAL OF PROFESSIONS

The organization of scientific work and the social position which it gives to the research worker are among the characteristics of our time. The days of the amateur have gone for good and a person such as Fr Nollet, whom contemporary engravings show conducting experiments in static electricity in a drawing room among the most leisured people of the day, is inconceivable in our own times. A modern priest starts a course of evening classes or an apprenticeship centre. The *physics room*, with its bric-à-brac of old-fashioned apparatus, has been replaced by the *laboratory* in which a research technique comes into existence. For, and this too is characteristic of our time, the relations between science and technology have been reversed. In the last century, science placed itself at the service of technology. The best example of this is provided by thermodynamics, the science invented by Sadi Carnot for the express purpose of perfecting the steam engine. It is a fact that Carnot's ideas, by linking the transformation of heat into work with the existence and the amount of variation in temperature between a warm and a cold source, namely the boiler and the condenser, gave a direction to research and determined the whole evolution of thermal machinery down to our own days.

At present the scientist devotes himself to the invention of techniques which may be of service to scientific research. And it is a fact that the branch of research which appears to be the most disinterested of all, namely, research not on industrial machinery but on the properties of the elementary constituent particles of matter, is precisely that which requires the most complex and gigantic machines, such as the particle accelerators. The recent inauguration at Meyrin, at the Centre européen de recherches nucléaires (C.E.R.N.) of a 29,000 million electron-volt proton synchrotron, whose circular track (in which the particles revolve) has a diameter of no less than 200 metres, is one of the finest achievements of science. It took four years to build and required the services of some hundred specialists. Its importance is far greater than that of the explosion of an atomic bomb.

The synchrotron is supplemented by a whole series of apparatus, in particular by the Wilson cloud chambers and the bubble chambers in which are traced the paths of atomic debris produced by the impact of nuclei projected at very high speed on to an appropriate target. This target may also be a photographic plate and then the paths of the disintegrated particles are inscribed in a thin layer of silver salts in the form of mysterious stars.

The theorists, whose task is to reflect on the results obtained and to direct research, are surrounded by a mass of technologists who have to make observable by various methods the events which occur in ever increasing numbers when the atom's structure is analysed after the application of high-powered projectiles.

These remarks are not intended to suppress the distinction between disinterested science and its applications. The scientist seeks above all to know the material world and leaves others to apply the body of knowledge thus acquired for utilitarian purposes and for the greater benefit of mankind. But independently of applications which add nothing to knowledge, the latter today requires the use of extremely powerful means whose proportions contrast sharply with the simplicity of the earliest experiments which dealt only with the most obvious aspect of material bodies and in particular with their movement at low speeds in space.

Classical chemistry, which only came into existence as an organized science in the nineteenth century, was already employing greater forces of energy than those of the ballistic machines of the ancients. Yet it was not until the advent of the theory of relativity and the appearance on the scene of nuclear energy that it became possible to suspect that there was a mysterious link between matter and energy, and to understand that the resistance set up by matter to any modification of its motion is in proportion to its energy. The static conception of science has been succeeded by a dynamic one according to which knowledge is already power before the technologists begin to specialize, before there is any division between contemplation and action. The mathematician himself has to use machines and the scope of his science depends on their power. Science has become a profession in its own right.

Science is the most universal of professions and this universality constitutes its title to nobility. To Descartes must go the credit for having insisted long ago that "the explanation of appliances", whatever their apparent diversity, revealed one single principle. It is true that statics only deals with one particular problem, that of the conditions of equilibrium in a material body. Descartes was fully conscious of this when he admitted that the problem of dynamics involved "the whole system of the universe". Since Descartes, the number of principles has continually increased, as have the number of universal constants and the number of elementary particles. Yet reduction to unity remains a fundamental desire of science and nothing reveals this more clearly than the research which has followed Einstein's ideas, and whose aim is to provide a synthesis of gravitation and electro-magnetism in one single system of equations. This produces a close dependence between what is known as *fundamental research* and the multiplicity of the applications of science that gives rise to the diversity of professions among which human activity is shared. A basic form of teaching, whose framework is mathematics, is necessary today for all who wish to assimilate the various techniques which govern the majority of skilled trades. It is this which justifies the considerable development of technical training today in most countries.

But this development demands as its counterpart that the teaching of the sciences should be accompanied by a *scientific culture*. We shall thus try to avoid the danger of a narrow concept of the universe and of life, a concept which reduces them to the single realm of recurring facts and neglects the irreplaceable part played by persons, who are by definition unique. And this scientific culture compensates for the corresponding narrowness of an exclusively literary humanism.

If scientific knowledge is to acquire this culture, it must not remain confined to the objective study of facts and laws, it must move inwards through reflecting on the conditions which make it possible for the mind to apprehend facts and laws. This reflection may proceed in two directions. The first is more rational and leads to the study of epistemology and the philosophy of science. The second is more existential, and leads to the history of the sciences. These two disciplines reveal the universal aspect of science by freeing it from the many and highly developed relationships which define its various fields.

It is much to be desired that this emphasis on the cultural aspect should go hand in hand with the elementary teaching of the sciences, and especially of mathematics which so often discourages children because of its abstract character, as well as because their teachers do not try to arouse the interest of their pupils by showing them the concrete origins of the ideas in question and their elementary relationships.

Among the disciplines which form part of fundamental research, there are two that reveal most clearly the universal scope of science. I refer on the one hand to rational mechanics with its two developments, relativity and wave mechanics; and, on the other hand, to the chemistry of the atom centred around Mendeleieff's classification and the more extended classification of nuclear species. Anyone who has grasped the main lines of these two disciplines could take a legitimate pride in viewing the material universe as a whole and then in reflecting upon the question of its accessibility to the mind. And this, according to Einstein, is the formidable problem which the very existence of science itself implies.

It is for the philosopher to find the solution, at least the philosopher who is willing to learn. But there can be no doubt that the ultimate answer must be provided by the Christian.

In the second chapter of this book I invited the reader to meditate on the fact that, during the larger part of his earthly life, Christ of his own will practised a trade, and we have seen that, during his public life, his teaching in the form of parables revealed the interest he took in the various trades in which his compatriots were engaged. As a fellow worker he had watched the sower, the harvester, the master of the vineyard and the workmen he engaged, and they are the source of those comparisons with which he clothed the highest truths and invited men of good will to seek above all the kingdom of God.

There is a lesson here for Christians. In Graeco-Latin antiquity, trades were practised by slaves and for a free man to engage in manual work would have seemed degrading. The science in which the Greek genius revealed itself was essentially contemplative and culminated in the series of geometrical theorems which conveys the knowledge of the figures freely constructed in space by the mind. Apart from a few timid attempts by Archimedes, the idea of mechanics, that is, a theoretical science emerging from the study of machines used by artisans, did not arise. There was no link between science and the trades.

Among the Jews, on the other hand, manual work was honoured. Whether in connection with the construction of the Ark of the Covenant or the building of Solomon's Temple, Scripture praises the skilled men who collaborated in the work. God took an interest in their labour and granted to them, as a gift from heaven, the talents they used for his glory. Further, Genesis shows us God himself at work on a task which lasted a whole week and was followed by rest on the seventh day. Human work is destined to complete the work thus interrupted, by exploiting the riches of creation. Moreover, the providential ordering of the world is also a work in itself and it was in imitation of his Father that Christ willed, with the visible submission of a son, to work and so to set us an example: "My Father worketh until now, and I work." This example, as we have seen, was followed by St Paul, who inculcated it in his turn in his pagan converts. The Christian is to work and so provide for his own sustenance and practise almsgiving. It is by collaborating in the building of the earthly city that he prepares himself to recover in a better city all the human and cosmic values transfigured by the resurrection. Time labours for eternity.

The trade practised by Christ at Nazareth was that of an artisan and so had little in common with the task of the scientist. We have already explained the reason for this and we do no more than provide a brief reminder here. The mission of the incarnate Son of God was strictly limited in space and time by the will of his Father. Jesus worked among his compatriots and adopted their methods; he had no intention of astonishing them by inventions or precocious marvels. But the mission of the Holy Spirit, which came after his own, is marked by a universal character which explains the rapid propagation of the Gospel in the Mediterranean world. This universal character meant that the infant Church was open to all the movements of ideas and all the tasks she encountered in her rapid expansion. St Paul is both the agent and privileged witness of this universalism. The dominant trait in his character is the sympathetic welcome he gave to all that was noble and great around him. Hence he quotes the Greek poets in his speech on the Areopagus and uses them as his authority for speaking of God. The idea of a Christendom which would be a realization on earth of the City of God, preceding and preparing for the heavenly city, haunted the Middle Ages. To it we owe the notion of a type of wisdom extending not only to the liberal arts but to all the professions, since they are all the work of man's hands as well as of his mind.

Modern science, through its universal character which makes it the necessary basis of all human techniques, has taken over the rôle of this medieval wisdom and has brought it to the acme of its expansion. Rationalization, due especially to the general use of mathematical method, should not make us lose sight of the cosmic character of science which has become evident through recent progress in astronomy and astronautics. The whole universe, which is God's work entrusted by him to man, has become the ultimate objective of scientific endeavour. The redemption wrought by Christ is to be brought to bear on this whole universe as the place in which dwells redeemed mankind. The Christian, following the example of St Paul, cannot therefore keep aloof from it, since, according to the Apostle, this material world itself awaits its deliverance from the slavery of sin.

CONCLUSIONS

My purpose in this book has been to examine the problem raised by the question, "Is Christianity uninterested in science?" by viewing it from different angles.

When I say that the answer to the question is in the negative I do not intend to deny that there is a strictly secular concept of science which is foreign to Christianity without however being necessarily hostile to it. In my view, it was characteristic of Greek science, which sought the rational evidence obtained by way of demonstration and was confined to an élite freed by the slave system from all preoccupation with the technique of the crafts which ensure man's material existence.

This concept is still found today. It was this type of science that Ernest Renan declared would command our future, while Ferdinand Brunetière proclaimed that it was already bankrupt. In any case, it deserves neither this excessive adulation nor this humiliation. In the view of those who practise it, its total disinterestedness in regard to human activity is a title to nobility, but it deliberately closes its eyes to the order of charity and so the Christian, who has in mind the "one thing necessary", cannot be interested in it.

Although I do not disown the part played in history by what Renan called "the miracle of Greece", I am of opinion that the origins of modern science are rather to be found in the rise of mechanics, whose basic notions are those of *force*, *work* and *energy*, all of which evoke human action and aim to make it effective. Doubtless, in order to play their part, these notions have had to be given precise definitions and to be integrated into a body of demonstration inspired by the Greek ideal. But however rational mechanics has become with the passage of time, it has not ceased to be a branch of physics, that is, of the science of nature. The adventure of the non-Euclidean geometries even shows what an attraction has been exercised on the Greek ideal by this effort towards a synthetic view of the universe as included in a context of new notions regarding space and time.

Mechanics, which emerged from a theory of machines, succeeded in imposing its rational framework on all the branches of physics one by one, beginning with thermo-dynamics, until one of them, electro-magnetism, has in its turn revolutionized physics by means of relativity dynamics.

New machines, infinitely more complex and efficient than those which prompted the speculations of Galileo and Descartes, have been invented and placed at the service of science which has contracted an indissoluble alliance with technology. By breaking with the Greek contempt for the trades, science has today become the most universal of professions, and this universalism assures it a place of honour in contemporary culture side by side with classical humanism, whose scale of values it completes, by giving to man a new vision of the universe.

What then, we may ask, is the relation of this science and the part it plays in human progress, to the kingdom which Christ came on earth to proclaim? Does our work on earth contribute to bringing into being the city of the future? If not, what is its relation to this city?

The first answer comes if we consider the terrestrial world in which our history evolves as a sign, imperfect though it is, of the world to come. The Christian welcomes joyfully and lovingly the tasks of life, but while he performs them, he preserves his faith and hope in a world to come out of all proportion to the world of the present which is doomed to destruction. The rôle of material realities is then to symbolize spiritual realities. This lesson seems to emerge from the teaching of the Gospel parables. The world in which we live is only the shadow or the image of the world to come; Newman asked that on his grave should be inscribed the words, *Ex umbris et imaginibus in Veritatem.*

Yet it is the Christian's duty to make the shadow less deep, to make the image more perfect, and this justifies his endeavour to promote human progress in this world and especially by means of science. But between this progress and the kingdom of God, between time and eternity there is no continuity. Just as for each man death is the end of his daily task and a sudden ushering into the presence of God, so too for the whole human race the day of the Lord will put an end to history and bring about the final coming of the kingdom of God, the descent on to the earth of the heavenly Jerusalem.

This answer, which is fairly common among Catholic and Protestant theologians, seems to me gravely inadequate. It does less than justice to the reality of the mystery of the Incarnation. No doubt Christ did use material realities in order to raise the minds of his hearers to the spiritual realities he was revealing to them, but this was possible only because in himself, and by virtue of his union with the Godhead, matter had in a sense become spiritualized and placed totally at the service of his divine mission. And we may surely say that the power at his disposal and which he exercised only for the purposes of love, shows us that the forces of the material world were dominated by him for the greater benefit of his fellow countrymen.

Science does not possess this miraculous power, which he now grants in a small degree only to a few privileged witnesses; yet we cannot fail to believe that the Man-God is interested in the efforts of science to fight disease and to increase the expectation of life, since he severely reproached the Pharisees for their indifference in this respect, wholly preoccupied as they were with a purely legal sanctity.

During his hidden life, when he abstained from all miraculous healing, the holiness of Christ was expressed in the perfect way he plied his trade (as I have explained, in line with the techniques of his time) and placed himself at the service of his fellow citizens, while ensuring their daily bread for himself and his mother.

Today the risen Christ shares, at the right hand of the Father, in the providential government of the whole universe and, as St John bears witness in his Apocalypse, it is to him that the development of human history is entrusted; this is symbolized by the opening of the sealed book. In the succession of civilizations, Christ presides over the circumstances which make possible the gradual realization of the fullness of his mystical Body. As a theologian has written:

> All the victories of thought and of art (and we add those of science) over matter, with its unwieldy and opaque nature, are Christ's own work, for Scripture tells us that all was made by him and that his domain goes beyond the frontiers of the Church, his body in the strict sense, and is exercised over all "powers", over the whole universe. Thus our purely human achievements, provided there is nothing sinful about them— *quaecumque sancta, quaecumque amabilia*—are the expression and the revelation of his kingship. Above all, they inwardly prepare for the final perfection of his body. As we all believe, each individual existence will continue in eternity the habits of thought acquired in this life in the secular order. And may not the same be said of humanity as a whole? We are entitled to think that the City of God will doubtless owe some features of its final shape to the traits and characteristics the historical civilizations have imprinted on our earthly cities.[1]

It is easy to see that the spirituality of the Catholic scientist may profit greatly from this Christian vision of secular history

[1] L. Malevez, S.J., "La vision chrétienne de l'histoire", in *Nouvelle Revue Théologique* (1949), pp. 260–1.

and that it will be a source of strength to him in his professional task.

Yet we must take into account the twofold mystery of sin
and of the Cross. A theology of the Incarnation would not be
genuine without a theology of Redemption. "Was it not to be
expected that the Christ should undergo these sufferings, and
enter so into his glory"? And Christ was given to us above
all as our Saviour.

The existence of sin in the world is so obvious that there is
no need to insist upon it. The real force of this objection, in
my view, arises from the fact that the denial of God is usually
accompanied by the placing of a premium on material values
even to the extent of excluding spirituality as an ultimate
cause and end. An atheist world is necessarily a (pseudo-)
scientific world. Hence science is held responsible for atheism
—an only too facile conclusion. The disorder in men's wills
involves the law of the Cross and calls upon the Christian to
agree to give up in this world the search for the full development of his own personality and for mastery over the universe.
He will know that his sacrifice will bear fruit in another life.

But let us not forget that, according to St John, the Father
of the Christian family himself prunes the vine, whose task is
to accept this partial death since it will earn for it an increase
of fruitfulness. Whatever legitimate efforts we may make to
improve the conditions of our own and our brethren's lives in
this world, we must be aware of and accept our defects and
our failures, in the knowledge that they are an inevitable result
of sin and a warning given to us that it is impossible fully to
reach in this world the ultimate destiny which is ours. It is in
this personal acceptance of failure that the law of Christian
renunciation essentially consists, and it is compatible with a
persistent effort to alleviate the sufferings of others.

To this renunciation we must add the austere nature of our
work. The successes and the moments of enthusiasm for some

particular discovery have had to be prepared for by years of work demanding a constant application to tasks that are deadly dull, monotonous and continual. Science therefore in its constant progress, produced at the cost of pain and travail, remains exposed not only to temporary setbacks but to the possibility of that betrayal of its civilizing ideals which reveals its link with this world of sin. The Christian scientist must be convinced of his own responsibility and must seek in his faith and in the practice of charity the remedy for a danger that is only too real. But, once this danger is recognized and withstood, the Christian scientist must become aware that he is working for the coming of the City of God to the very extent that he fulfils his task in the service of the city of man.

We may therefore conclude that in spite of failures and obstacles and the temporary deviations they cause, the divine plan does not cease to be fulfilled in the unfolding of history; the command, given before the Fall that man should continue the benevolent activity of God's creative will by fruitful labour undertaken for God's glory, is still valid for a humanity redeemed.

SELECT BIBLIOGRAPHY

In this series: NÉDONCELLE, M.: *Is There a Christian Philosophy?*

BIVORT DE LA SAUDÉE, J. de (Editor): *God, Man and the Universe*, London, Burns & Oates, and New York, Kenedy, 1954.

BURTT, E. A.: *The Metaphysics of Sir Isaac Newton, An Essay on the Metaphysical Foundation of Modern Science*, New York, Humanities Press, 1952.

CHARDIN, Teilhard de: *The Phenomenon of Man*, London, Collins, and New York, Harper, 1959.

DUBARLE, D., O.P.: *Scientific Humanism and Christian Thought*, translated by Reginald F. Trevett, London, Blackfriars, 1956.

EINSTEIN, A.: *The World as I See It*, translated by Alan Harris, London, Bodley Head, and New York, Corvici, 1934.

KEYNES, J. M.: "Newton the Man" in *Newton Tercentenary Celebrations*, Cambridge and New York, Cambridge University Press, 1947.

LONERGAN, B. J. F.: *Insight*, London and New York, Longmans, 1957.

MARITAIN, J.: *The Degrees of Knowledge*, London, Bles, and New York, Scribner, 1958; *Science and Wisdom*, London, Bles, and New York, Scribner, 1944.

TAYLOR, F. Sherwood: *Short History of Science and Scientific Thought*, New York, Norton, 1957; *The Century of Science*, London, The Scientific Book Club, 1943.

THAYER, H. S.: *Newton's Philosophy of Nature*, New York, Hafner, 1953.

WIENER, P. P.: *Readings in the Philosophy of Science*, New York, Scribner, 1953.

The Twentieth Century Encyclopedia of Catholicism

The number of each volume indicates its place in the over-all series and not the order of publication.

TWENTIETH CENTURY ENCYCLOPEDIA OF CATHOLICISM

All titles are subject to change.